CROSS-SECTIONAL
Human Anatomy

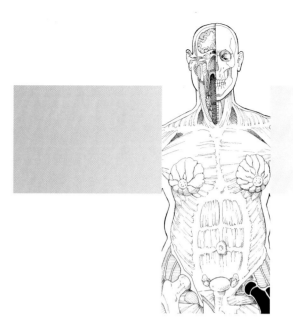

CROSS-SECTIONAL
Human Anatomy

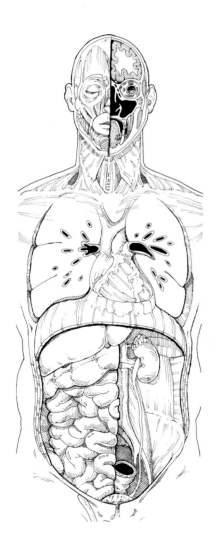

DAVID DEAN, PhD

Assistant Professor
Director, Imaging Laboratory
Department of Neurological Surgery
Case Western Reserve University
Cleveland, Ohio

THOMAS E. HERBENER, MD

Assistant Professor
Department of Radiology
University Hospitals of Cleveland
Cleveland, Ohio

Illustrations by: Daniel Knopsnyder

LIPPINCOTT WILLIAMS & WILKINS
A **Wolters Kluwer** Company

Philadelphia • Baltimore • New York • London
Buenos Aires • Hong Kong • Sydney • Tokyo

Editor: Paul J. Kelly
Managing Editor: Crystal Taylor
Marketing Manager: Jennifer Conrad
Project Editor: Jennifer D. Weir

351 West Camden Street
Baltimore, Maryland 21201-2436 USA

227 East Washington Square
Philadelphia, PA 19106

Printed in the United States of America

Library of Congress Cataloging-in-Publication Data
Dean, David, 1960-
    Cross-sectional human anatomy / David Dean, Thomas E. Herbener;
  illustrations by Daniel Knopsnyder.
      p.   cm.
    Includes index.
    ISBN 0-683-30385-6 (spiral bound)
    ISBN 0-7817-2674-3 (perfect bound)
    1. Human anatomy Atlases.   2. Tomography Atlases.   I. Herbener,
  Thomas E.   II. Title.
    [DNLM: 1. Anatomy, Regional.   2. Diagnostic Imaging.   QS 4 D281c
    2000]
    QM25.D43   2000
    611'.0022'2—dc21
    DNLM/DLC
    for Library of Congress   99-16455
                                                            CIP

The publishers have made every effort to trace the copyright holders for borrowed material. If they have inadvertently overlooked any, they will be pleased to make the necessary arrangements at the first opportunity.

To purchase additional copies of this book, call our customer service department at **(800) 638-3030** or fax orders to **(301) 824-7390**. For other book services, including chapter reprints and large quantity sales, ask for the Special Sales department.

For all other calls originating outside of the United States, please call **(301) 714-2324**.

Visit Lippincott Williams & Wilkins on the Internet: **http://www.lww.com**. Lippincott Williams & Wilkins customer service representatives are available from 8:30 am to 6:00 pm, EST, Monday through Friday, for telephone access.

99 00 01 02 03
1 2 3 4 5 6 7 8 9 10

FOREWORD

It is a great honor to write the foreword for this textbook on anatomy. Because the authors are in our institution, I am quite familiar with their excellent work and their dedication to high quality and accuracy. On first consideration, one might ask why would anyone produce a new text on anatomy when there are a number of anatomy books already available? The answer is quite obvious if one contemplates the nature of radiologic imaging, the state of medicine, and the very sophisticated state of the imaging sciences.

The practice of medicine has come to depend more and more on the examination of internal organs by imaging methods. If one takes a cynical or candid perspective, it almost seems naïve for a physician to do palpation of the body in an attempt to define maladies of internal organs. Imaging technologies using X-ray, ultrasound, magnetic waves, and radioisotopes can give precise anatomic delineation as well as function. The relevance of this observation is readily apparent if one recognizes how frequently patients in a hospital have an imaging study before they even have a physical examination.

With the exquisite anatomic display in imaging currently available and the progress being made in new technology, there is no question that the role of imaging will continue to grow. This growth and future potential dictates that anatomic texts continue to be revised to provide the most up-to-date references possible so that medical school teaching, clinicians, and radiologists maintain a high level of knowledge in anatomy and the imaging fields.

I applaud my colleagues for their remarkable diligence and efforts in producing this textbook. I believe it goes a long way in answering the need for current anatomic texts. I am proud to have been associated with the authors during this project.

John R. Haaga, MD
Chairman and
Theodore J. Castele University Professor
Case Western Reserve University
Department of Radiology
University Hospitals of Cleveland
Cleveland, Ohio

Primarily, this book is written for the first-year medical student. After an average of only 180 hours of gross anatomy (American Association of Medical Colleges), lecture, and laboratory experience this student becomes a clerk. During the clerk's year-long, whirlwind rotations through the various clinical departments of the teaching hospital, they are constantly surrounded by plain-film x-ray, computed tomography (CT), magnetic resonance (MR), and ultrasound images of the internal anatomy; however, clinical training demands leave little time to review the basic anatomy that would lend to interpreting these images. Most of the radiographic images today's clerk sees are CT and MR. These are tomographic (two-dimensional) slice images. Students often find that they do not learn to interpret radiological images until their residency. However, unless they are in radiology, residents encounter only a specialized subset of clinical films related to their mentors' radiological training in the distant past. In retrospect, the student realizes that the best time to have learned to identify anatomical structure in tomographic images was during gross anatomy.

A majority of medical students have probably studied tissue-based sectional images during their gross anatomy training. These are usually formaldehyde-preserved, band-sawed, axial cadaver slices encased in lucite that are mounted in the anatomy lab along with an assortment of radiographs. Often these slices are traced, labeled, and distributed to the students as study aids. In an attempt to impress, the new faculty member may label the key with minutiae on which even the instructors could not agree and that has no clinical relevance. However, fearing those lucite blocks on the practical examination, most medical students memorize—amidst the unpleasant smell of the anatomy laboratory and often the night before the examination—the key for each block. Observing these tortured beings year after year provided the motivation for this text.

As faculty, we were equally frustrated. Clearly, axially sectioned cadaveric material was an invaluable aid to the student as they attempted to transfer the knowledge gained in an anatomy lecture and dissection to the reading of tomographic radiographs. This interpretation exercise is a powerful test of the students' knowledge of the spatial relations, the surface morphology, and the internal structures that they are spending so much time studying. There is clearly a valuable experience to be had with band-sawed cadaver slices and random radiographs. Unfortunately, more often than not, many of the structures of most interest were within the 2″ cadaveric slab or destroyed by the thick saw blade. Perhaps they were on the other side of the lucite block, which is covered with air bubbles. Moreover, the lucite blocks are easily shattered into a disgusting mess. And, it may be difficult to make a quick pass of radiology reading room droppings and envision tomographic images that reasonably match the available axial cadaveric sections.

In 1991, beginning with the body donation of a 39-year-old Caucasian male who was a convicted murderer, the Visible Human project began at the University of Colorado Health Sciences Center. A 32-year-old Caucasian female cadaver was donated in 1993. Radiological data was created with commercial MR- and CT-scanning devices. Both types of scans were collected postmortem, one of the fresh cadaver, the other after freezing. No radiological data were collected prior to either individual's death. Immediately after MR- and CT-scanning, both cadavers were embedded in gelatin, frozen, and sliced. The male was sliced in millimeter increments, the female in 0.33-mm increments. As each layer was exposed, a color red-green-blue (RGB) photograph was taken, resulting in 1871 Visible Man and more than 5000 Visible Woman 24-bit color cryosection images at 2048 × 1216 resolution.

The Visible Human images offer a very high quality source of cadaveric cross-sectional images with lifelike colors. However, medical students do not have enough time amongst the 800 to 1000 hours that they must spend on gross anatomy to locate the best views of the relevant structures amongst the 8000 slices of Visible Human cryosection images. Someone had to go through these slices to select and label the "most" relevant sections to an efficient learning cross-sectional anatomy experience. In addition, location of well-matched, state of the art radiographs was also necessary. Combined, these images should assist the students to translate their reading, lecture, and cadaver dissection experience to the reading of axial MR and CT radiographs as well as other commonly used radiological diagnostic modalities (e.g., plain-film x-ray and ultrasound).

To make progress in this area we felt that high-quality cadaveric cross-sectional and radiographic images had to be put into the curriculum further ahead of the examination. The relevant set of cadaveric section and radiographic images need to be available for reference by the student during their anatomy reading, faculty lectures, and dissection laboratories. Having seen this atlas before their moment of need, a well-rested student would then be prepared, based not on memorization but rather on careful study of the anatomy, to enter a practical examination.

David Dean and Thomas Herbener
September 1999

ACKNOWLEDGMENTS

The authors are deeply indebted to Dr. John Haaga, Chair, of the Department of Radiology, University Hospitals of Cleveland/Case Western Reserve University Cleveland for assistance that made this project possible. Dr. Haaga carefully reviewed the first proposal of this book and suggested the addition of Dr. Thomas Herbener, a radiologist, to insure the usefulness of this text to medical students during their transition from basic to clinical science. Once work on this text was underway, Dr. Haaga graciously provided access to the Department's vast teaching collection. Dr. Haaga also made sure that we were able to produce local CT and MR patient data that would provide the closest possible match to the Visible Human cadaveric cryosection images after it was determined that the Visible Human cadaveric radiological data would not be a useful study aid for medical students.

After the submission of the book proposal to Lippincott Williams & Wilkins, this project received much direction from the insightful review of the project proposal by Drs. Robert Acland, Arthur Dalley, and Keith Moore. Their reviews and constructive comments improved the design of this book considerably. Meetings with them were arranged through the efforts of an energetic Acquisitions Editor, Ms. Jane Velker. Jane graciously passed the project to Mr. Paul Kelly, who saw it through to completion in 1999.

The authors would not have been able to produce this book without the perspicacious efforts of Mr. Daniel Knopsnyder. Dan's recent training as both a medical illustrator and anatomist were as essential to this project as his familiarity with cutting-edge visualization software, scanning, and color printing technology. Dan's activities bridged the selection and labeling of the cryosection and the radiological data so essential to this book. All art in and on this book either is his work or is the result of his collaboration with Lippincott Williams & Wilkins' production staff. Dan's style of illustration holds the middle ground between the nonanatomical geometries of scalable art and timeless, lifelike, proportionate art in the tradition of Grant's Atlas, Sabotta, and Pernkopf.

We also thank the organizers of the National Institutes of Health (NIH) Visible Human Project for their foresight into the needs of tomorrow's training physicians. We thank the principal investigators in that project for their careful work and attention to detail. We thank the many individuals who have studied the Visible Human data, produced internet-accessible resources, and provided us feedback at the annual NIH-sponsored Visible Human conferences.

Finally, we thank Dr. Vid Persaud, Department of Human Anatomy & Cell Science, the University of Manitoba, and Dr. Richard Drake, Department of Cell Biology, Neurobiology, and Anatomy, the University of Cincinnati, for their careful review of the final manuscript.

CONTENTS

CHAPTER 1

Introduction

CHAPTER 2

Thorax

CHAPTER 3

Abdomen

CHAPTER 8

Head

CHAPTER 9

Neck

CHAPTER 1

Introduction

This textbook is written to assist first-year medical students to transfer the spatial relations and surface morphology of human organ systems information they learn to the reading of tomographic (i.e., a two-dimensional cross-section) radiological grayscale images, primarily computer tomography (CT) and magnetic resonance (MR). Study of the surfaces found in radiological images requires the student to learn "normal" organ interrelations, surface shapes, and internal textures. The trend in medical education is clearly to link education more to clinical situations and less to basic science research efforts. This is by necessity. The amount of data available to inform the student's assessment of a patient's condition is growing rapidly. Part of this growth includes greater use and variety of tomographic radiographs in medicine.

TOMOGRAPHIC VIEWS OF THE BODY

The use of grayscale in radiographic images may seem a mystery to the new medical student. Grayscale is the representation of structures with different shades of gray, from completely black to completely white. Everyone is familiar with the interpretation of grayscale in plain film radiographs. X-ray radiation that strikes the film exposes it (black is exposed). Dense structures shield the x-ray beam, thus the most dense structures (e.g., bone and teeth) appear as bright (white) objects. In plain film radiographs the entire object imaged is projected onto a single piece of film. The grayscale in CT images is interpreted in the same

way, however these x-ray images result from radiographs that form a planar cut through the body. Unfortunately, because their component tissues are of similar density, inhomogeneous soft-tissue structures, such as muscles, brain, liver, heart, and kidney, often appear to be homogenous in plain film or tomographic (CT) radiographs.

The grayscale in MR is different. The brightest elements contain water, fat, or both. Thus soft-tissue organs and blood-filled structures appear bright. The fat and water in these structures are more susceptible to the magnetic fields interpreted by an MR scanner than is avascular cartilage or highly mineralized bone. Subtle differences in tissue chemistry provide great detail to the internal structures of the brain, heart, liver, and kidney. MR scanners and thus images from them are more expensive than CT images, however, the potential for remote imaging in MR has only begun to be tapped.

Ultrasound is finding ever more use in the imaging of near-surface structures, as well as of the heart through the esophagus and the prostate through the rectum. Nuclear medicine (e.g., gamma cameras, densitometers, and single-photon emission CT) and functional imaging (e.g., magnetoelectroencephalography, functional MR, and positron emission tomography) is still the work of specialist radiologists. Viewing images from multiple modalities either side by side or coregistering them, when possible, into one view is often useful. Although it requires more powerful computer software and hardware, three-dimensional (3D) rendering of surfaces seen in MR and CT volume images is becoming more useful clinically. For example, neurosurgeons now commonly use 3D CT and 3D MR images to guide them in the operating room or as a basis for a radiosurgical plan. Indeed, neurosurgeons use volume brain images (a stack of CT or MR slice images that together represent the cranial cavity) at all stages of the patient's care cycle (i.e., diagnosis, treatment plan-

ning, intraoperative treatment, and postoperative outcomes assessment). Already, in the operating rooms of a few dozen hospitals, a CT or an MR scanner is used in the assessment of surgical progress. It is not hard to imagine a future in which most specialty fields approach or overtake the neurosurgeon's use of tomographic and 3D radiographic images.

WHEN SHOULD ONE BEGIN A STUDY OF CROSS-SECTIONAL ANATOMY?

Core knowledge of the anatomy is essential to the development of an ability to interpret what is seen in tomographic CT or MR radiographs. After a careful textbook study, an anatomy laboratory dissection of a single cadaver, and especially a comparison of that dissection with that of fellow students, medical students' best opportunity to test their understanding of the "normal" 3D morphology of human organ systems is the cross-sectional anatomy. Students mentally test themselves when they begin to infer through what portion of the organs seen in an MR or a CT the visualized plane passes. (Fig. 1-1).

Immediately after having learned the terminology and perused stereotypic illustrations in the anatomy text is the time to begin studying cross-sectional anatomy. Study of cross-sectional images requires intuitive understanding of the relation of the "anatomical position" of the body to the "anatomical planes" of the body. Figure 1-1 presents a rendering of the Visible Human in the anatomical position (one might prefer to have the heels touching).

To use this book effectively the student must be familiar with other anatomical terms that infer directions relative to the human body in anatomical position. The key to each image includes the

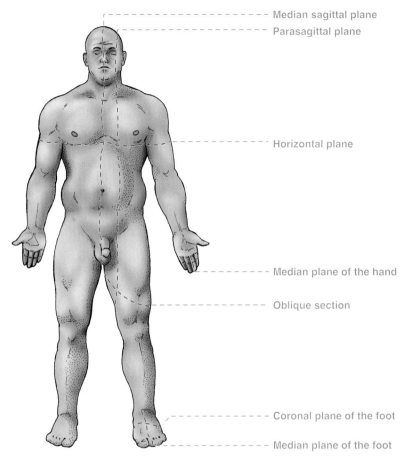

Median sagittal plane
Parasagittal plane

Horizontal plane

Median plane of the hand

Oblique section

Coronal plane of the foot

Median plane of the foot

FIGURE 1-1 **Anatomical Position and Planes.** Visualization of the anatomical position and planes is equally favorable whether the patient is erect or laying on a table. Note that the arms are at the side, with the thumbs positioned laterally. The midsagittal or median-sagittal plane bisects the body into right and left sides. Any plane parallel to it is a parasagittal plane. Except for in the foot, the long axis of the body would be cut by an axial plane that is at a right angle (i.e., orthogonal) to a sagittal plane. Axial planes through the body, not the foot, are also referred to as horizontal planes as they are parallel to the ground in the erect person. Horizontal planes divide the body into upper and lower portions. At a right angle to both of these planes is a coronal plane. Coronal planes divide the body into front and back portions. An axial plane through the foot (i.e., one that is at a right angle to the long axis of the foot) is the same as a coronal plane, not the horizontal plane as elsewhere in the body. Oblique planes are those that are not parallel to any of the three standard planes used to describe the body in anatomical position. The median planes of the hand and the foot cut down the longest ray. This is the third (middle) finger in the hand and the second toe in the foot.

directions anterior and posterior and right and left. Strictly speaking, anterior and posterior refer to the mouth end and the anus end, respectively. The heart, stomach, and rectum are found primarily on the left side; the liver is found primarily on the right. Proximal is toward the trunk; distal is away from it. Cranial is toward the head; caudal is toward the tail. Within the head, rostral refers to being toward the nose. Ventral refers to belly side; dorsal refers to the back side. The dorsal side of the foot actually appears continuous with the ventral surface in the adult human body, although embryologically it was dorsal. The plantar side refers to the sole of the foot; volar refers to either the sole of the foot or the palm of the hand.

CHAPTER ORGANIZATION

The chapters of this book are arranged in the same order as Moore and Dalley's "Clinically Oriented Anatomy," Agur's "Grants Atlas," and Sauerland's "Grant's Dissector." It should be possible for students to read those books simultaneously as they prepare for class and laboratory. As Figure 1-2 presents, the chapters are color coded in the table of contents and on the edge of the book in the same schema used by Dr. Grant's famous trilogy.

All chapters in this book begin with an introduction. Initially, concepts regarding the shapes of the organs found in these contained regions are also presented. After that there is a brief, section-by-section summary of the chapter contents. The sections are organized around a plate from the Visible Man or the Visible Woman image databases. Each section consists of a right-left pair of pages. There is a color-coded illustration at the leftmost side of the Visible Man or Woman with an axial plane drawn through it to indicate the level of the cryosection image. In addition to an orientation icon indicating right, left, anterior, and posterior, there is a key for the labels seen on the Visible Man or Woman cryosection image.

Associated with the Visible Man or Woman cryosection image and key is a pen-and-ink outline image that matches the cryosection image. This outline image includes textures intended to represent the type of tissue (muscle, bone, fat, organ, etc.) seen in the cryosection. Because the Visible Human radiographic data was taken posthumously, we decided not to use the Visible Human CT or MR images. We did not think they were similar to images that medical students are likely to begin seeing during their clinical rotations. Instead we chose to collect the most similar images we could find from patients. Given the rapid advances made in scanner quality, we also attempted to use state-of-the-art imaging protocols that provide the clearest structures. In almost

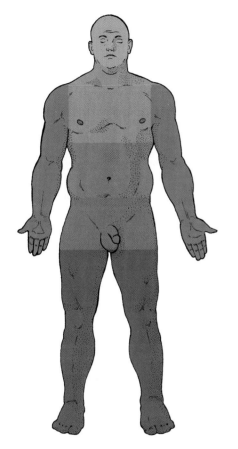

FIGURE 1-2 **Color Coding of Chapters.** Location of chapters in this book is indicated by color strips that can be seen when the book is closed. They are the same colors used to indicate the chapters in Grant's Atlas. Key: Chapter 2—Thorax; Chapter 3—Abdomen; Chapter 4—Pelvis/Perineum; Chapter 5—Lower Extremity; Chapter 6—Back; Chapter 7—Upper Extremity; Chapter 8—Head; and Chapter 9—Neck.

every case, we provide a corresponding CT image. In many cases, we also provide a corresponding MR image. Where appropriate we have included commonly used diagnostic images, especially when a plane other than axial is called for by the salient anatomy in that section's region of interest.

Some of the diagnostic images include contrast agents intended to highlight the internal structure or the surface of the organ of interest. There are separate textual descriptions of the cryosection, corresponding CT, and corresponding MR (or diagnostic) images. All textual descriptions traverse the image anterior to posterior.

LINKS TO THE REST OF THE CURRICULUM: LECTURE, LAB, AND THE WEB

The Visible Man or Woman identification number that allows relation of the page to any teaching aids that become available for that section is found in the Professor's lecture, acetates mounted in the laboratory, and relevant CD-ROM-, DVD-ROM-, or web-based software and images. At this writing there are dozens of websites that attempt to provide material for studying the Visible Human data. Unfortunately, few at this time provide corresponding patient radiological data to go with the cryosection images. And, of course, at this time, there is no cryosection data with comparable resolution, color, or both from other individuals to compare with the Visible Man and Woman data.

Carefully monitor your time spent surfing the web for Visible Human, radiographic imaging, or purely cross-sectional anatomy sites. Most are proffering commercial products. Many companies have developed viewers that, for the most part, link reconstructed frontal and sagittal views of the Visible Man and Woman to the enormous volumes of color and radiological data that one can download, free of charge, from the Visible Human website at the National Institutes of Health (NIH) website. This too is a lengthy exercise with time better spent obtaining the Visible Human disc.

Perhaps the best use of the web for the medical student attempting to learn cross-sectional anatomy is to peruse the 3D renderings of various organ systems that are continuously being produced from the Visible Human cryosection and radiological data. The following is a subsampling of Visible Human websites that highlight (as of January 1999) such 3D renderings that may be useful to medical students:

(1) The National Library of Medicine: www.nlm.nih.gov/research/visible
The central repository of links to websites presenting projects based on the Visible Human data. Many of the links found here in 1998 were out of date; however, this is probably the best place for the itinerant Visible Human data explorer to begin.

(2) Voxel-Man (University of Hamburg, Germany)
http://www.uke.uni-hamburg.de/institute/imdm/idv/vmjr/
The highest quality 3D renderings of the Visible Human data known to these authors. A great deal of effort has been made to make these data useful to the medical student.

(3) Marching Through the Visible Man (Schenectady, NY, U.S.)
http://www.crd.ge.com/esl/cgsp/projects/vm/
Prepared by General Electric's Research Scientist, Bill Lorensen. One of the first and best sites to assist the student to locate slice images from 3D renderings of the Visible Man and Woman.

(4) Stanford Visible Man and Woman Viewers (Palo Alto, CA, U.S.)
http://summit-3.stanford.edu/
Very good fee-free viewers for the Visible Man and Woman data.

(5) The Visible Human Slice Server (Lausanne, Switzerland)
http://visiblehuman.epfl.ch/
A browser that allows selection of oblique views of the Visible Male color cryosection data and thereby generates the replanarized views on demand.

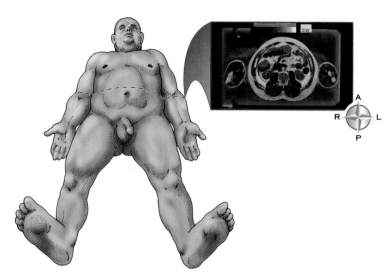

FIGURE 1-3 Reading Tomographic Images. In this book, the radiographic convention of always looking at the slide information from below is used. That meant reversing right and left in all the images as the Visible Man and Woman were actually sliced and photographed from the top down. Fortunately, the thin slices and surrounding gel leave almost no impression that the slice faces inferiorly rather than superiorly. As with plain film radiographs, this convention also insures that the patient's left and right are reversed from that of the viewer. Small anatomic directional arrows (like that seen here) along with every cryosection and matching radiographic image are used as a reminder of this fact. Note that the blue gel has been removed from the original cryosection images and only the body segment under discussion is illustrated in the sections presented in this book. An original Visible Man image is shown here with both the arms, the trunk, and the encasing blue gel. Key: A, anterior; L, left; P, posterior; and R, right.

(6) Center for Human Simulation (Boulder, CO, U.S.)
http://www.uchsc.edu/sm/chs/
Sponsored by Anatomical Visual Inc., a company formed to distribute labeled sections and 3D renderings of the Visible Human data.

(7) Workshop Anatomy for the Internet (Mainz, Germany)
http://www.uni-mainz.de/FB/Medizin/Anatomie/workshop/vishuman/Eready.html
Presents a number of labeled Visible Human cryosection and radiological images.

(8) The Queensland University (Australia) Digital Anatomy Laboratory
http://www.dal.qut.edu.au/DALhome.html
As of this writing, this site provided an interface linking a 3D rendering of the knee to Visible Man axial slice images.

CHAPTER 2

Thorax

INTRODUCTION

The superior mediastinum, inferior to the cupolae of the lungs and the root of the neck (see Chapter 9 for structures in these latter spaces) are reviewed in Plate 2-1 of this chapter. Among the great vessels shown are the brachiocephalic, the left common carotid, and the left subclavian arteries just superior to their exit from the arch of the aorta. The long traverse of the left braciocephalic vein versus the shorter right brachiocephalic vein is seen. The roof of the arch of the aorta can be clearly visualized in Plate 2-2. This plate also presents the intervertebral disc between thoracic levels four and five that is significant clinically. It is palpated anteriorly at the manubriosternal angle. In addition to the base of the aortic arch and superior mediastinum, other structures are found at this level. These include the bifurcation of the trachea and the arch of the azygos vein.

Note that the right atrium is visible through most of the thoracic series. The pulmonary trunk is present in Plate 2-5. In Plate 2-6 we see the left atrium and a clear view of the right ventricle. The massive walls of the left ventricle Plates 2-8 and 2-9. Its hemielliptical chamber is longitudinally sectioned in Plate 2-8. It is recommended that medical students carefully review the corresponding computed tomography (CT) images of the heart structures. Clinically, these are currently the most commonly used diagnostic images of the heart and great vessels.

For more careful study, Figures 2-1–2-6 presents a zoomed-in (magnified) view of the great vessels and the heart chambers seen in Plates 2-1 through 2-6. Knowledge of the locations of transparent structures allows one to infer their location with standard contrast (window) setting such as the bronchi azygos vein below its arch. However, these structures may be highlighted on alternative contrast settings as seen in the diagnostic CT image in Plate 2-5.

Oblique views of the heart are more easily taken with magnetic resonance (MR) or ultrasound. An

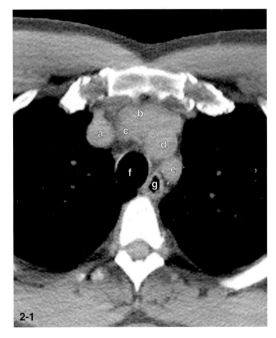
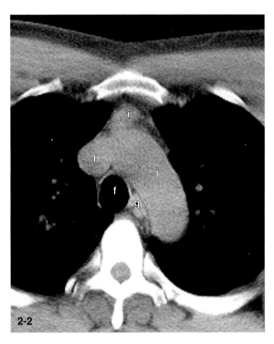

FIGURES 2-1–2-6 Axial CT of the Great Vessels and Heart Chambers. This heart series shows magnified CT images for which the field of view has not been centered on the heart; instead, the image of this area has been magnified. Therefore, if this zoomed in view were taken as the original field of view, the boundaries between the labeled structures would be much clearer. a, right brachiocephalic vein; b, left brachiocephalic vein; c, brachiocephalic artery; d, left common carotid artery; e, left subclavian artery; f, trachea; g, esophagus; h, superior vena cava; i, thymus gland or parathymic fat; j, aortic arch; k, transverse pericardial sinus; l, ascending aorta; m, descending aorta; n, arch of the azygos vein; o, left pulmonary artery; p, right pulmonary artery; q, left bronchus; r, right bronchus; s, pulmonary trunk; t, right atrium; u, right pulmonary vein; v, left pulmonary vein; w, left atrium; x, right ventricle; y, left ventricle; z, spleen; aa, intercostal arteries; bb, right aortic cusp; cc, anterior aortic cusp; dd, right internal thoracic artery; ee, splenic artery. (*continued*)

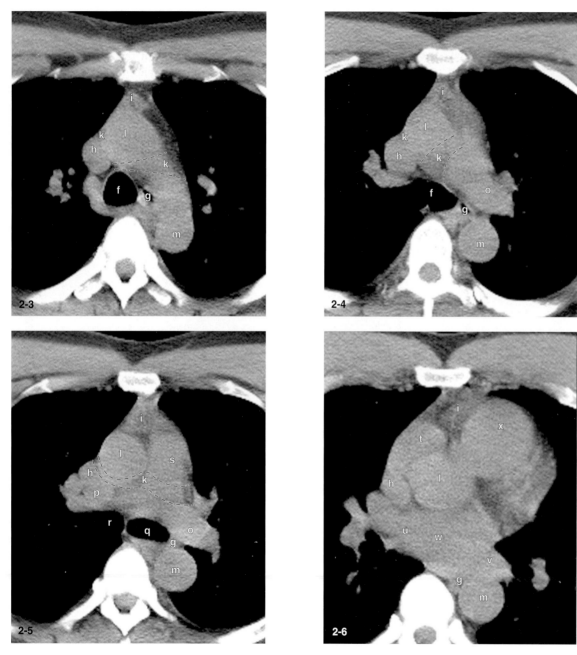

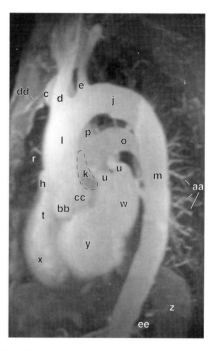

FIGURE 2-7 **Oblique Sagittal View.** MR angiogram of the heart and the great vessels. The right pulmonary veins and superior vena cava are also visible. a, right brachiocephalic vein; b, right brachiocephalic artery; c, left common carotid artery; d, left subclavian artery; e, left subclavian artery; f, trachea; g, esophagus; h, superior vena cava; i, thymus gland or parathymic fat; j, aortic arch; k, transverse pericardial sinus; l, ascending aorta; m, descending aorta; n, arch of the azygos vein; o, left pulmonary artery; p, right pulmonary artery; q, left bronchus; r, right bronchus; s, pulmonary trunk; t, right atrium; u, right pulmonary vein; v, left pulmonary vein; w, left atrium; x, right ventricle; y, left ventricle; z, spleen; aa, intercostal arteries; bb, anterior aortic cusp; cc, posterior aortic cusp; dd, right internal thoracic artery; ee, splenic artery.

FIGURES 2-1–2-6 Axial CT of the Great Vessels and Heart Chambers.—*Continued.*

oblique, but largely, sagittal view of heart is seen in Figure 2-2. CT, MR, and subtraction angiography are all powerful means to study occlusion of the vessels of the heart. Three-dimensional surface and volume imaging of the heart may soon become as commonplace clinically as it is now for the brain, skull, and pelvis.

Plates 2-8 and 2-9 well illustrate the usual relation, from left to right, of the descending aorta, thoracic duct, and azygos vein, found posterior to the esophagus. It is easy to remember the 8-10-12 rule for diaphragmatic traverse, with the inferior vena cava passing through at the eighth (or the ninth) thoracic level, the esophagus at the tenth thoracic level, and the aorta at the twelfth thoracic level. Keep in mind that this is different than the level schema for the inferior-most extent of the uninspired lungs at midclavicular, midaxial, and midscapular positions. When fully inspired, the lungs can expand into the costodiaphragmatic space about either diaphragmatic dome in accordance with an 8-10-12 schema.

PLATE 2-1 SUPERIOR MEDIASTINUM *(Visible Man 1350)*

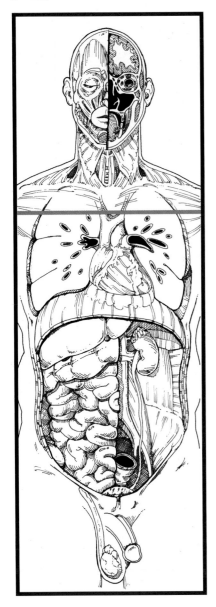

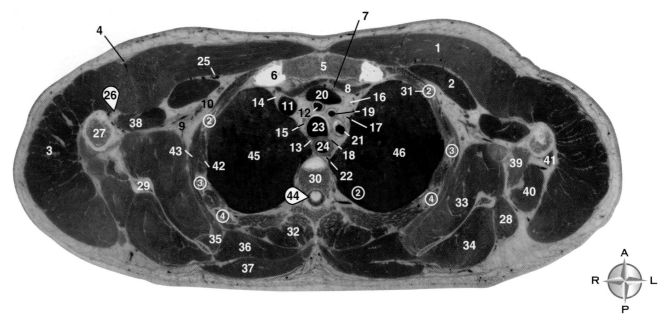

1	Pectoralis major muscle	21	Left subclavian artery	38	Biceps and coracobrachialis muscle

1 Pectoralis major muscle
2 Pectoralis minor muscle
3 Deltoid muscle
4 Cephalic vein
5 Manubrium
6 First rib cartilage
7 Thymic fat
8 Sternohyoid muscle
9 Axillary vein
10 Axillary artery
11 Right brachiocephalic vein
12 Brachiocephalic artery
13 Right recurrent laryngeal nerve
14 Right phrenic nerve
15 Right vagus nerve
16 Left phrenic nerve
17 Left vagus nerve
18 Left recurrent laryngeal nerve
19 Left common carotid artery
20 Left brachiocephalic vein

21 Left subclavian artery
22 Thoracic duct
23 Trachea
24 Esophagus
25 Thoracoacromial vessels
26 Long head of the biceps muscle and tendon
27 Humerus
28 Teres major muscle
29 Scapula
30 Third thoracic vertebra
31 Rib (corresponding rib numbers are within circles)
32 Erector spinae muscle
33 Subscapularis muscle
34 Infraspinatus muscle
35 Serratus anterior muscle
36 Rhomboid major muscle
37 Trapezius muscle

38 Biceps and coracobrachialis muscle
39 Latissimus dorsi muscle
40 Long head of the triceps muscle
41 Lateral head of the triceps muscle
42 Internal intercostal muscle
43 External intercostal muscle
44 Spinal cord
45 Upper lobe of the right lung
46 Upper lobe of the left lung

RADIOGRAPHIC KEY

a Right mainstem bronchus
b Left mainstem bronchus
c Tracheobronchial lymph nodes
d Carina of the trachea
e Middle lobe of the right lung
f Inferior lobe of the right lung
g Inferior lobe of the left lung
h Aortic arch

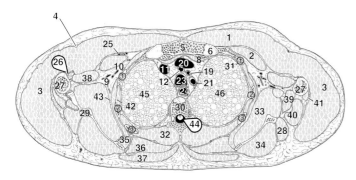

PLATE 2-1 SUPERIOR MEDIASTINUM *(Visible Man 1350)*

Corresponding CT. Virtually the same structures and level as the cryosection. Note that the trachea is to the right rather than anterior of the esophagus. Note the indentation of the skin under the vertebral spinous processes in this patient. The Visible Man cadaver cryosection has lost this tonus.

Cryosection. This section passes through the third thoracic vertebral level. The first costal cartilage (bright white area) articulates with the manubrium anteriorly, just inferior to the clavicle. This level is immediately superior to the great arch of the aorta in the superior mediastinum. The pericardial reflection surrounds the three upward passing great vessels, the brachiocephalic artery, the left common carotid artery, and the left subclavian artery. The two brachiocephalic veins merge somewhat inferiorly. Similarly, the azygos vein is draining into the arch of the azygos seen inferiorly. Note that, unlike the anterior tracheal ring, the posterior membrane can extend anteriorly into the airway as a bolus passes posteriorly through the esophagus.

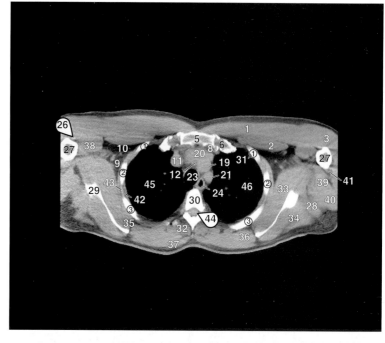

Diagnostic Image. Coronal CT reconstruction of posterior mediastinum. This reconstruction is done digitally by computer to allow a coronal view from standard transverse or axial CT scans. Note the anatomic relationships of various mediastinal structures in this plane.

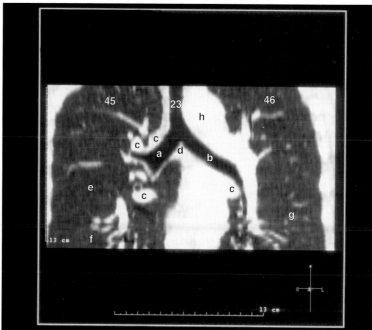

PLATE 2-2 AORTIC ARCH *(Visible Man 1368)*

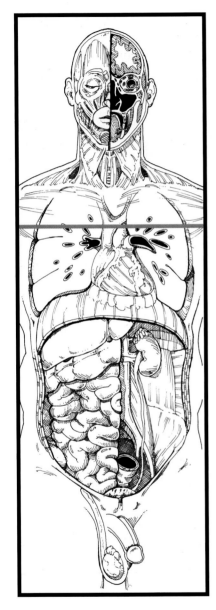

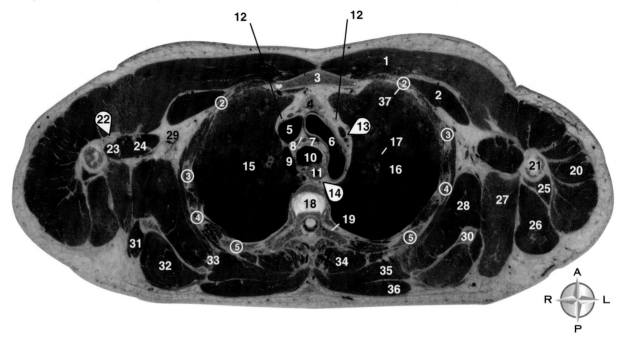

1 Pectoralis major muscle	**19** Costotransverse joint of the fifth thoracic vertebra and the fifth rib	**35** Rhomboid minor muscle
2 Pectoralis minor muscle	**20** Deltoid muscle	**36** Trapezius muscle
3 Sternum	**21** Humerus	**37** Rib (corresponding rib numbers are within circles)
4 Thymus	**22** Tendon of the long head of the biceps muscle	
5 Superior vena cava	**23** Long head of the biceps muscle	**RADIOGRAPHIC KEY**
6 Aortic arch	**24** Biceps and coracobrachialis muscle	**a** Left common carotid
7 Transverse pericardial sinus	**25** Lateral head of the triceps muscle	**b** Brachiocephalic artery
8 Right vagus nerve	**26** Long head of the triceps muscle	**c** Left subclavian artery
9 Azygos vein entering the superior vena cava	**27** Latissimus dorsi muscle	**d** Ascending aorta
10 Trachea	**28** Subscapularis muscle	**e** Right pulmonary vein
11 Esophagus	**29** Subscapular vessels	**f** Left pulmonary vein
12 Left vagus nerve	**30** Scapula	**g** Left pulmonary artery
13 Pericardiophrenic vessels	**31** Teres minor muscle	**h** Pulmonary trunk
14 Thoracic duct	**32** Infraspinatus muscle	**i** Left atrium
15 Right lung	**33** Serratus anterior muscle	**j** Left ventricle
16 Left lung	**34** Erector spinae muscles	**k** Diaphragm
17 Bronchial vessels		**l** Liver
18 Intervertebral disc of the fourth and the fifth vertebrae		**m** Aneurysm

PLATE 2-2 AORTIC ARCH (Visible Man 1368)

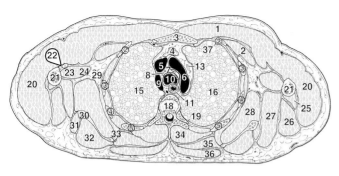

Cryosection. This section passes through both the fourth and fifth thoracic vertebra, a plane commonly palpated at the manubriosternal junction (angle) anteriorly. The superior mediastinum transitions here to the anterior, middle, and posterior mediastinal compartments. The great arch of the aorta is transected. The two brachiocephalic veins have coalesced into the superior vena cava. The roof of the azygos vein is seen draining into the superior vena cava. The trachea is nearly at its widest point at the level of its bifurcation. The left recurrent laryngeal nerve is seen in association with the trachea. The right and left vagal trunks are clearly visualized anterior to the phrenic nerve passing within the pericaridial sac surrounding the middle mediastinum.

Corresponding CT. Note that the thymic region in the anterior mediastinum is clearly visualized because it is surrounded by fat, which is dark on CT, in the adult. Similarly, the posterior thoracic wall region of the azygos vein and the thoracic duct is highlighted by surrounding fat and the anteriorly overlying esophagus. The link that the serratus anterior provides between the scapula and the rib cage is more easily visualized in this CT than in the cryosection.

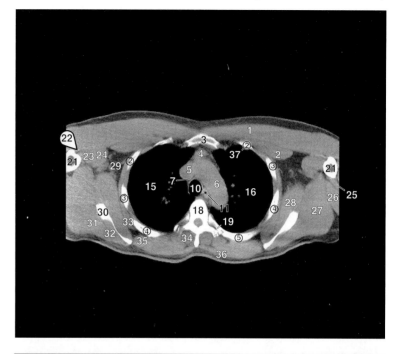

Diagnostic Image. MR angiogram in a sagittal oblique plane. Intravenous contrast was given and a rapid sequence MRI was performed in this plane showing vascular structures as bright. Note the relationship of the aorta, arch, origins of great vessels, pulmonary vessels, and cardiac chambers. This patient has a large focal aneurysm, "m", arising off the ascending aorta. (Key: S, superior; R, right; I, inferior; L, left.)

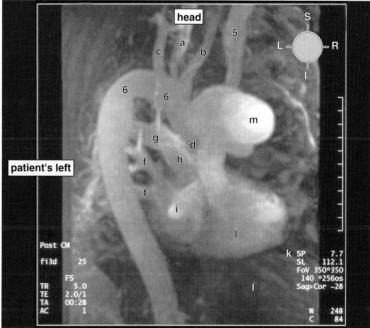

PLATE 2-3 AZYGOS SYSTEM *(Visible Man 1372)*

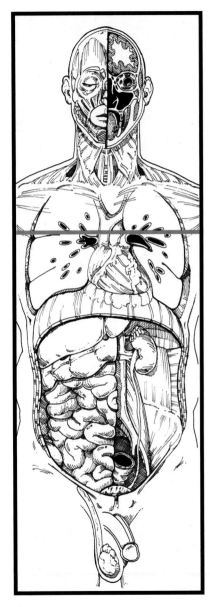

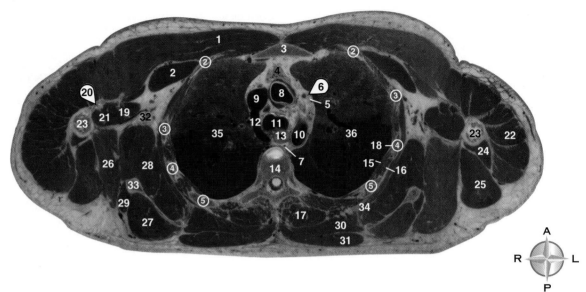

1	Pectoralis major muscle	15	Internal intercostal muscles
2	Pectoralis minor muscle	16	External intercostal muscles
3	Sternum	17	Erector spinae muscle
4	Thymus	18	Rib (corresponding rib numbers are within circles)
5	Phrenic nerve		
6	Pericardiophrenic vessels and nerve	19	Biceps and coracobrachialis muscle
7	Thoracic duct	20	Long head of the biceps tendon
8	Ascending aorta	21	Long head of the biceps muscle
9	Superior vena cava	22	Deltoid muscle
10	Descending aorta	23	Humerus
11	Bifurcation of the trachea	24	Lateral head of the triceps muscle
12	Arch of the azygos vein	25	Long head of the triceps muscle
13	Esophagus	26	Latissimus dorsi muscle
14	Fifth thoracic vertebra	27	Infraspinatus muscle

28	Subscapularis muscle
29	Teres minor muscle
30	Rhomboid minor muscle
31	Trapezius muscle
32	Brachial plexus
33	Scapula
34	Serratus anterior muscle
35	Right lung
36	Left lung

RADIOGRAPHIC KEY

a	Lymph nodes of the AP window
b	Breast

PLATE 2-3 AZYGOS SYSTEM *(Visible Man 1372)*

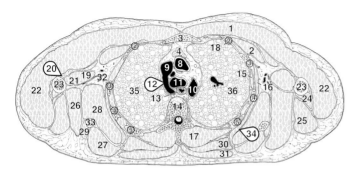

Cryosection. This section passes through the fifth thoracic vertebral level. As usual, this level presents the inferior-most view of the azygos trunk arching over the root of the right lung, draining anteriorly to the superior vena cava. The rest of the azygos (primary, right side) and the hemiazygos (secondary, left side) system is highly variable. A significant, normal, thymic mass is present. The trachea has completely bifurcated. The four sides of the pyramidal, fatty axilla are visible.

Corresponding CT. Virtually the same images as the cryosection. Note that the trachea is to the right of, rather than anterior to, the esophagus. Note the indentation of the skin under the vertebral spinous processes in this patient. The Visible Man cadaver cryosection has lost this tonus.

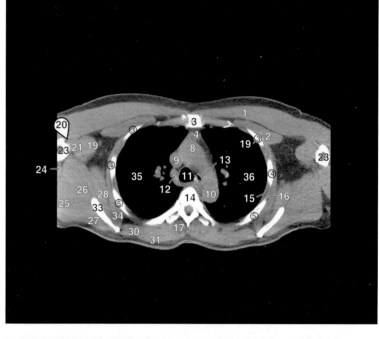

Diagnostic Image. Slightly further inferior view of fifth thoracic level in a female. Note arms were raised above the head as is typical in clinical thoracic image studies. Note the multiple lymph nodes in the AP window. Note the fatty tissue of the left breast.

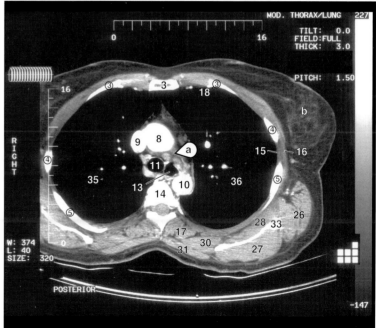

PLATE 2-4 TRANSVERSE PERICARDIAL SINUS *(Visible Man 1381)*

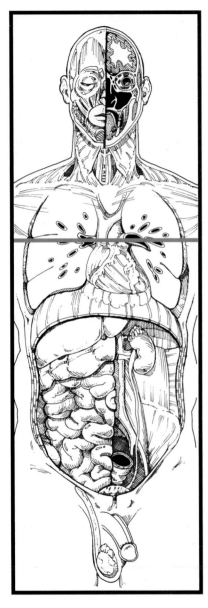

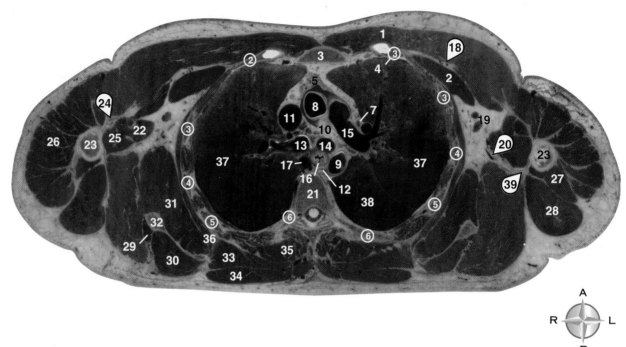

1 Pectoralis major muscle
2 Pectoralis minor muscle
3 Sternum
4 Rib and costal cartilage (corresponding rib numbers are within circles)
5 Thymus
7 Pericardiophrenic vessels and nerve
8 Ascending aorta
9 Descending aorta
10 Transverse pericardial sinus
11 Superior vena cava
12 Thoracic duct
13 Right bronchus
14 Left bronchus
15 Pulmonary artery

16 Esophagus
17 Azygos vein
18 Thoracoacromial vein
19 Subscapular vessels and nerve
20 Axillary vessels
21 Fifth thoracic vertebra
22 Biceps and coracobrachialis muscle
23 Humerus
24 Long head of the biceps tendon
25 Long head of the biceps muscle
26 Deltoid muscle
27 Lateral head of the triceps
28 Long head of the triceps
29 Teres major muscle
30 Infraspinatus muscle

31 Subscapularis muscle
32 Scapula
33 Rhomboid major muscle
34 Trapezius muscle
35 Erector spinae muscle
36 Serratus anterior muscle
37 Superior lobe of the lung
38 Inferior lobe of the lung
39 Radial nerve

RADIOGRAPHIC KEY

a Thymic region of the anterior mediastinum
b Superior segmental bronchus
c Right pulmonary artery
d Tumor

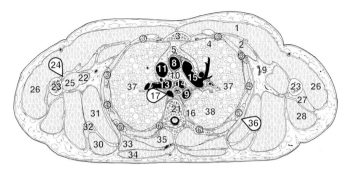

PLATE 2-4 TRANSVERSE PERICARDIAL SINUS *(Visible Man 1381)*

Cryosection. This section passes through the inferior portion of the fifth thoracic vertebra. Note that the zygapophyses between T5 and T6 are visible in this section. The transverse pericardial sinus is clearly seen posterior to the aorta and the superior vena cava and anterior to the left mainstem bronchus. This level transects the pulmonary trunk as it gives off the left pulmonary artery. The shorter right bronchus has already branched.

Corresponding CT. Again, it is seen that the thymus region is highlighted by the fat in the anterior mediastinum that is held in place by the pericardiosternal ligaments. The esophagus is found lateral to the trachea instead of posterior as in the cryosection and it is collapsed. There is spatial variability in the relations of these somewhat mobile structures.

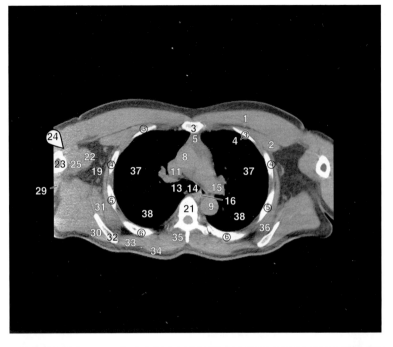

Diagnostic Image. CT right-lung window that highlights the carina, the right pulmonary arteries, and a tumor seen laterally, which is a lung carcinoma.

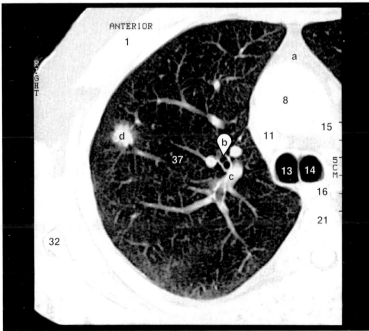

PLATE 2-5 PULMONARY ARTERIES *(Visible Man 1388)*

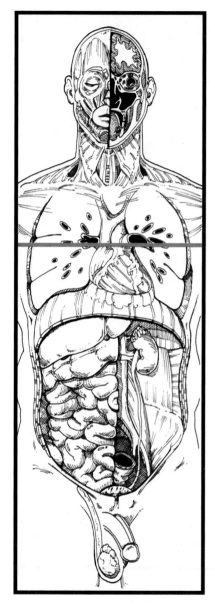

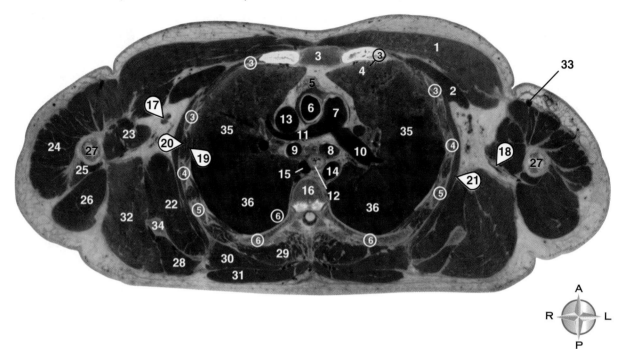

1   Pectoralis major muscle
2   Pectoralis minor muscle
3   Sternum
4   Rib and costal cartilage
    (corresponding rib numbers are
    within circles)
5   Thymus
6   Ascending aorta
7   Pulmonary trunk
8   Left bronchus
9   Right bronchus
10 Left pulmonary artery
11 Right pulmonary artery
12 Esophagus
13 Superior vena cava

14 Descending aorta
15 Azygos vein
16 Fifth thoracic vertebra
17 Subscapular vessels and nerve
18 Axillary vessels
19 Internal intercostal muscle
20 External intercostal muscle
21 Serratus anterior muscle
22 Subscapularis muscle
23 Biceps and coracobrachialis
    muscle
24 Deltoid muscle
25 Lateral head of the triceps
26 Long head of the triceps
27 Humerus

28 Infraspinatus muscle
29 Erector spinae muscle
30 Rhomboid major muscle
31 Trapezius muscle
32 Latissimus dorsi muscle
33 Cephalic vein
34 Scapula
35 Superior lobe of the lung
36 Inferior lobe of the lung

RADIOGRAPHIC KEY

a   Subcutaneous adipose tissue
b   Pulmonary embolism
c   Fifth thoracic vertebra with
    pathology

PLATE 2-5 PULMONARY ARTERIES *(Visible Man 1388)*

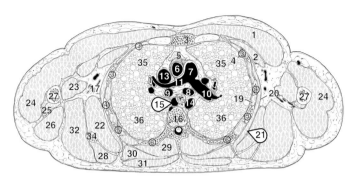

Cryosection. This section passes through the inferior, anterior centrum, portion of the sixth thoracic vertebra. Posteriorly the head of the sixth rib is seen articulating with the sixth thoracic vertebra. The dominant feature of this section is the full view of right (long) and left (short) pulmonary arteries entering the hila of both lungs. The pulmonary trunk branches into the pulmonary arteries just under the arch of the aorta that is held in place by the ligamentum venonsum, which is the same fetal structure that causes the descent of the left recurrent laryngeal nerve. This level also affords the most substantial view of the teres major and serratus anterior muscles.

Corresponding CT. Virtually the same image as the cryosection. The anterior mediastinum, including thymic remnants, is highlighted by the surrounding fat held in place by the sternopericardial ligaments. The esophagus is found lateral, not posterior, to the trachea as in the cryosection. The spatial variability of these relations is to be expected of mobile structures that are normally and temporally distended.

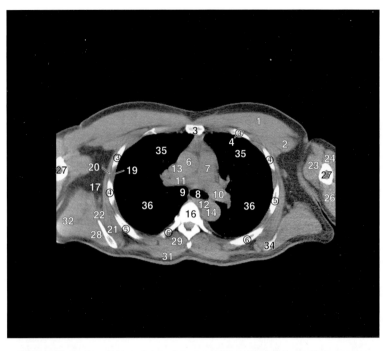

Diagnostic Image. Virtually the same image as the cryosection. This is a CT scan with intravenous contrast that makes vascular structures turn bright or enhance. Note the filling defect in the left pulmonary artery consistent with a thrombus in the artery or pulmonary embolus. Note the bony spurs or osteophytes extending off the fifth thoracic vertebra.

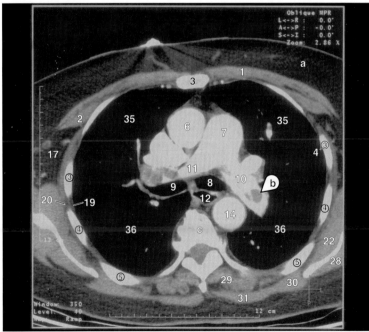

PLATE 2-6 LEFT AND RIGHT AURICLES (*Visible Man 1415*)

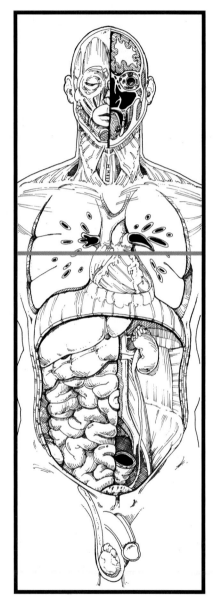

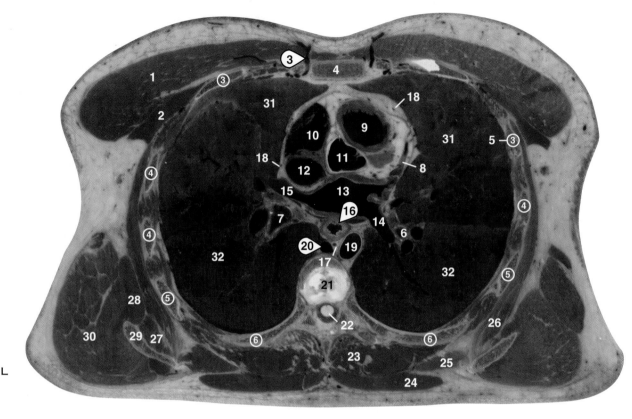

1	Pectoralis major muscle	16	Esophagus	30	Latissimus dorsi muscle
2	Pectoralis minor muscle	17	Thoracic duct	31	Superior lobe of the lung
3	Anterior Perforating Branch of internal thoracic artery	18	Pericardiophrenic vessels and nerve	32	Inferior lobe of the lung

1 Pectoralis major muscle
2 Pectoralis minor muscle
3 Anterior Perforating Branch of internal thoracic artery
4 Sternum
5 Rib (corresponding rib numbers are within circles)
6 Left bronchus
7 Right bronchus
8 Left coronary artery
9 Right ventricle
10 Right atrium
11 Ascending aorta
12 Superior vena cava
13 Left atrium
14 Left pulmonary veins
15 Right pulmonary veins

16 Esophagus
17 Thoracic duct
18 Pericardiophrenic vessels and nerve
19 Descending aorta
20 Azygos vein
21 Intervertebral disk of the fifth and the sixth thoracic vertebrae
22 Spinal cord
23 Erector spinae muscle
24 Trapezius muscle
25 Rhomboid major muscle
26 Serratus anterior muscle
27 Subscapularis muscle
28 Teres major muscle
29 Scapula

30 Latissimus dorsi muscle
31 Superior lobe of the lung
32 Inferior lobe of the lung

RADIOGRAPHIC KEY

a Right subclavian artery
b Right vertebral artery
c Right common carotid
d Brachiocephalic artery
e Left common carotid artery
f Left subclavian artery
g Left vertebral artery
h Left pulmonary artery
i Right pulmonary artery
j Left ventricle
k Liver

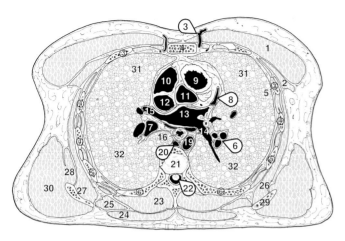

PLATE 2-6 LEFT AND RIGHT AURICLES *(Visible Man 1415)*

Corresponding CT. Two atria, right ventricle, and aorta are the prominent structures of the heart. The blood-filled left ventricle is below this plane, thus accounting for its reduced radiopacity.

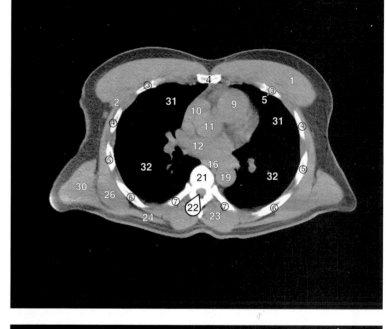

Cryosection. This section passes through the intervertebral disk spanning the fifth and the sixth thoracic vertebra. The anterior lip of the T5 centrum is visible. A gap in the false rib costal cartilages allows the internal thoracic arterial branches to become the superior epigastric arteries. Similarly, superior epigastric veins are draining the anterior thoracic wall into the internal thoracic veins. The two atrial chambers are prominently viewed, as is the right ventricle. The superior surface of the muscular left ventricle is just in view. A long section through the left coronary artery is present. The lateral margins of the right aortic cusps are visible, although the cusp itself is not. The thoracic duct is firmly appressed among the descending aorta, esophagus, and azygos vein.

Diagnostic Image. Coronal MR angiography of the heart, showing pulmonary arteries and veins (especially on the right), descending aorta, left ventricle, right brachiocephalic artery, left common carotid artery, both subclavian arteries, and both vertebral arteries. (Key: S, superior; L, left; I, inferior; R, right.)

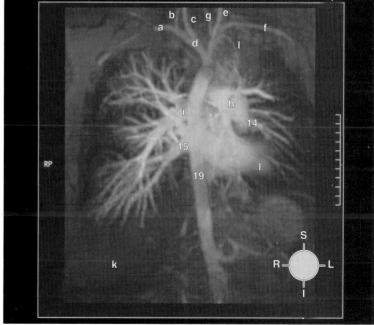

PLATE 2-7 RIGHT VENTRICLE (*Visible Man 1425*)

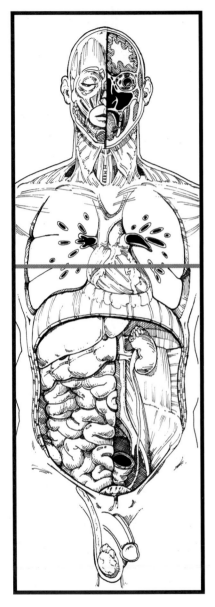

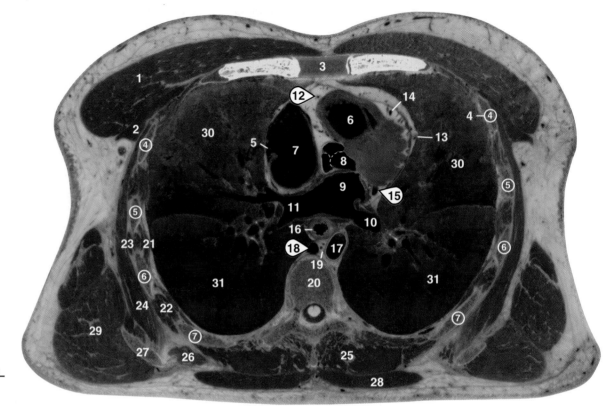

1 Pectoralis major muscle	**12** Right coronary artery	**24** Serratus anterior muscle
2 Pectoralis minor muscle	**13** Pericardiophrenic vessels and nerve	**25** Erector spinae muscle
3 Sternum	**14** Anterior interventricular artery	**26** Rhomboid major muscle
4 Rib and costal cartilage (corresponding rib numbers are within circles)	**15** Left circumflex artery	**27** Scapula
	16 Esophagus	**28** Trapezius muscle
5 Right auricle	**17** Descending aorta	**29** Latissimus dorsi muscle
6 Right ventricle	**18** Azygos vein	**30** Superior lobe of the lung
7 Right atrium	**19** Thoracic duct	**31** Inferior lobe of the lung
8 Ascending aorta with cusps illustrated	**20** Eighth thoracic vertebra	
	21 Innermost intercostal muscle	## RADIOGRAPHIC KEY
9 Left atrium	**22** Internal intercostal muscle	**a** Left coronary artery
10 Left pulmonary veins	**23** External intercostal muscle	**b** Anterior interventricular artery
11 Right pulmonary veins		**c** Aorta

PLATE 2-7 RIGHT VENTRICLE *(Visible Man 1425)*

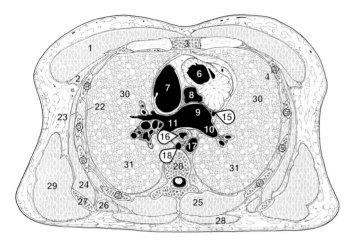

Corresponding CT. Slightly higher section than the cryosection. Both the seventh and the eighth vertebra and rib heads are seen. The two atria, right ventricle, and aorta are the prominent heart structures. A long traverse of the right coronary artery is present.

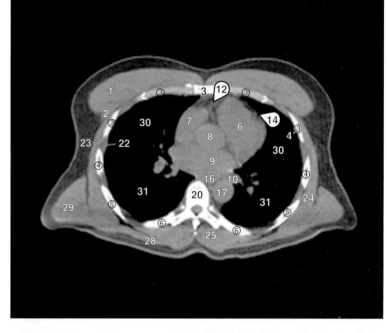

Cryosection. This section passes through the middle of the eighth thoracic vertebra. It gives a primary view of the right ventricle. This cryosection also shows that the thickened muscular roof of the left ventricle is commonly found at the same horizontal level as the base of the left atrium. The right coronary and the left anterior interventricular (left anterior descending) arteries can be seen. All three aortic cusp margins can be seen. The artist has added lines illustrating the location of these three cusps. The base of the superior vena cava is highlighted by the crista terminalis separating the right atrium from its auricle.

Diagnostic Image. Coronary angiogram shows a lateral view of the heart. A catheter was placed into the descending aorta from a femoral arterial approach. Contrast was injected into the left coronary artery. The apex of the heart is cut off where the anterior interventricular artery reflects to the posterior side to anastomose with the posterior interventricular artery. The anterior interventricular artery is clinically referred to as the LAD or left anterior descending artery.

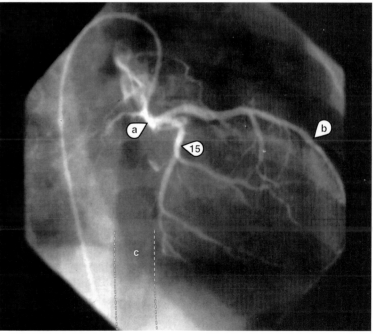

21

PLATE 2-8 ATRIOVENTRICULAR VALVES *(Visible Man 1439)*

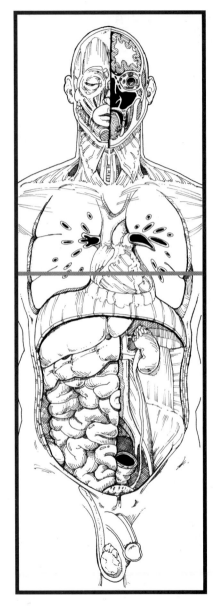

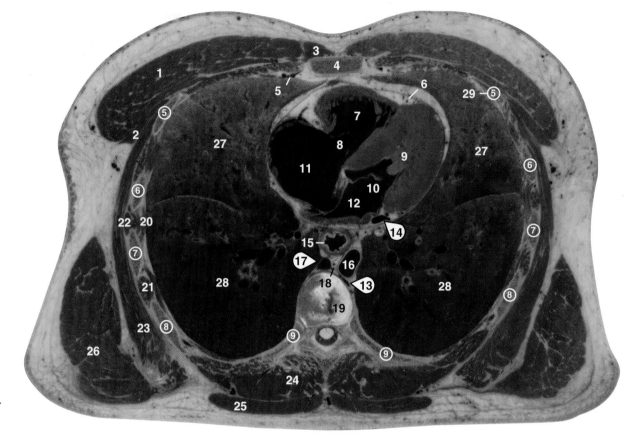

1 Pectoralis major muscle
2 Pectoralis minor muscle
3 Rectus abdominis muscle
4 Sternum
5 Superior epigastric vessels

6 Left anterior interventricular artery
7 Right ventricle
8 Tricuspid valve
9 Left ventricle
10 Mitral valve
11 Right atrium
12 Left atrium
13 Hemizygos vein
14 Left circumflex artery
15 Esophagus
16 Descending aorta
17 Azygos vein
18 Thoracic duct
19 Intervertebral disc of the eighth
and the ninth thoracic vertebrae

20 Innermost intercostal muscle
21 Internal intercostal muscle
22 External intercostal muscle
23 Serratus anterior muscle
24 Erector spinae muscle
25 Trapezius muscle
26 Latissimus dorsi muscle
27 Superior lobe of the lung
28 Inferior lobe of the lung
29 Rib (corresponding rib numbers
are within circles)

RADIOGRAPHIC KEY

a Larynx (area of the vocal folds)
b Trachea

c Thyroid gland
d Right subclavian vein
e Left subclavian vein
f Right internal jugular vein
g Left internal jugular vein
h Right brachiocephalic vein
i Left brachiocephalic vein
j Pulmonary artery
k Right lobe of the liver
l Left lobe of the liver
m Gallbladder
n Transverse colon
o Stomach
p Humerus
q Clavicle
r Ascending aorta

PLATE 2-8 ATRIOVENTRICULAR VALVES *(Visible Man 1439)*

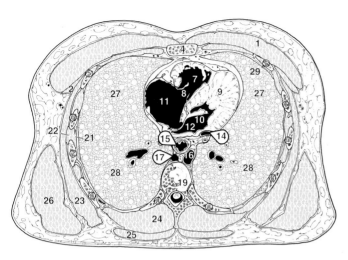

Cryosection. This section passes through the intervertebral disc between the eighth and the ninth thoracic vertebrae. This level shows both atrioventricular valve openings, but the valve cusps are not well visualized. Missing portions of the tricuspid valve, between the right atrium and the right ventricle, are especially apparent, as it is too expansive. It appears there is a free piece of papillary muscle and one strand of chordae tendinae present in the mitral valve between the left atrium and the left ventricle. The hemizygos vein is present below the descending aorta.

Corresponding CT. Slightly higher section, at the eighth thoracic vertebra, than the cryosection image. All four chambers of the heart are prominently visualized. However, with little radiolucency in between and no intravenous contrast, it is difficult to differentiate them. Note the compression of the esophageal lumen near the esophageal sphincter just superior to the cardiac orifice of the stomach.

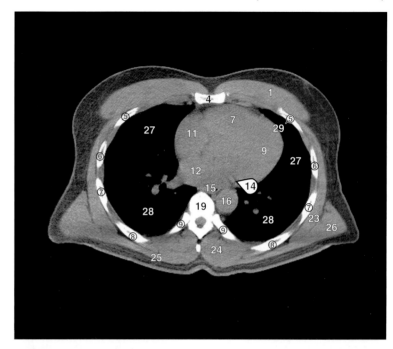

Diagnostic Image. MR of an anteriorly placed coronal plane, visualizing the left ventricle wall and cavity. The aortic valve is marked by compression just inferior to the ascending aorta. The pulmonary artery is seen passing below the aorta. The difference in pleural cavity space available to the right and left lungs owing to the distribution of the heart in the thorax is apparent. The vessels in the base of the neck are veins and note their relationship. Because no intravenous contrast was given for this study and the type of MR sequence done, vessels are dark.

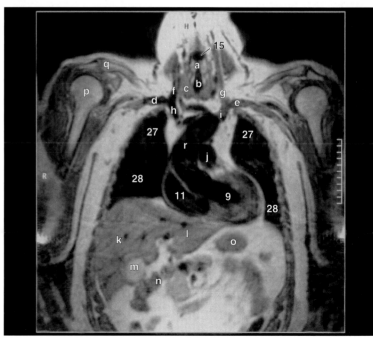

PLATE 2-9 SUPERIOR DIAPHRAGMATIC SURFACE *(Visible Woman 1449)*

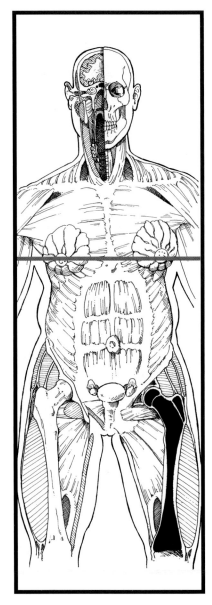

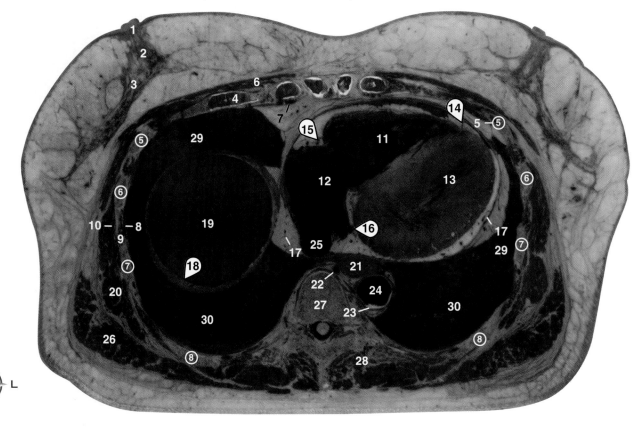

1 Nipple	12 Right atrium	21 Esophagus
2 Lactiferous ducts	13 Left ventricle	22 Azygos vein
3 Cooper's ligaments	14 Left anterior interventricular	23 Plaque on the internal surface of
4 Costal cartilage (calcified)	artery	the descending aorta
5 Rib (corresponding rib numbers	15 Right coronary artery	24 Descending aorta
are within circles)	16 Posterior interventricular artery	25 Inferior vena cava
6 Rectus abdominis muscle	17 Pericardiophrenic vessels and	26 Latissimus dorsi muscle
7 Superior epigastric vessels	nerve	27 Ninth thoracic vertebra
8 Innermost intercostal muscle	18 Right dome of the diaphragm	28 Erector spinae muscle
9 Internal intercostal muscle	19 Liver	29 Superior lobe of the lung
10 External intercostal muscle	20 Serratus anterior muscle	30 Inferior lobe of the lung
11 Right ventricle		

PLATE 2-9 SUPERIOR DIAPHRAGMATIC SURFACE *(Visible Woman 1449)*

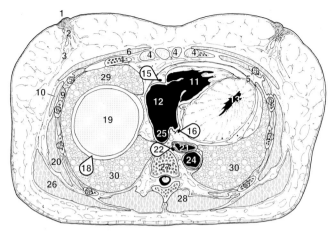

Corresponding CT. Section at the same level as the cryosection. It is also a female image. Note the lucencies within the lactiferous ducts of the left breast. As usual, this image was taken with arms raised over the head.

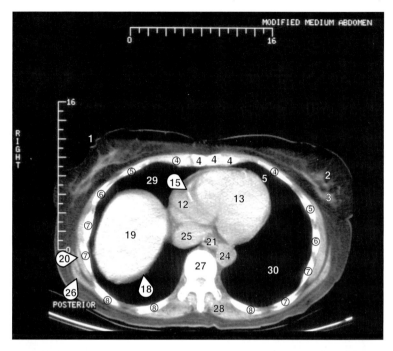

Cryosection. This section passes through the ninth thoracic vertebral level in this image from the Visible Woman data set. It also intersects the nipples of both breasts. Of the three major longitudinal structures passing between the thorax and the abdomen, the inferior vena cava passes through the diaphragm first, roughly at the base of the eighth thoracic vertebra. The esophagus usually traverses the diaphragm at the level of the tenth thoracic vertebra. The aorta usually traverses the diaphragm at the level of the twelfth thoracic vertebra. The right diaphragmatic hemidome is higher than the left owing to the protrusion of the liver.

Diagnostic Image. Mammograms of this type are usually a plain-film breast radiograph taken from the side. The darker portion of the breast represents fat. The whiter areas in the breast are areas of normal glandular tissue.

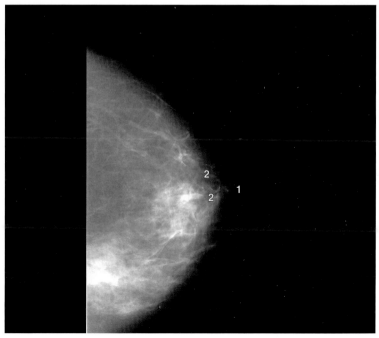

CHAPTER 3

Abdomen

INTRODUCTION

The diaphragm separates the thorax and the abdomen. It is helpful to keep in mind that this muscular membrane consists of two lateral domes with three central orifices. The costodiaphgragmatic recess, surrounding the right and the left diaphragmatic domes, extends inferiorly to the level of the twelfth thoracic vertebra. The broad diaphragmatic crura surrounding the aorta extend further inferiorly, approximately halfway down the lumbar vertebral column. The central (mediastinal) orifices occur regularly at the levels of the eighth thoracic (superior vena cava), tenth thoracic (esophagus), and twelfth thoracic vertebra (aorta). The anterior abdominal wall changes appearance from the thoracic intercostal and rib architecture to the rectus sheath and oblique muscles.

The two paravertebral gutters are deepest cranially and become shallower as one approaches the lordosis (ventral flexion) at the small of the back just above the lumbosacral joint between the fifth lumbar vertebra and the sacrum. The retroperitoneal suprarenal glands, kidneys, and spleen are found in these gutters. The left kidney is characteristically 0.5 to 1 vertebra (2 to 3 cm) higher on the left. It finds less resistance during its fetal ascent from the pelvis than the right kidney, which contacts the liver. Inferiorly, in the region of the small of the back, the inferior vena cava comes to overlie the descending aorta. Its common iliac tributaries usually join more superiorly than the descending aorta splits into common iliac branches.

The gastrointestinal tract of the abdomen is different from that of the thorax in the presence of the ventral (falciform ligament) and dorsal mesen-

teries. Embryological relations of the abdominal gut to the celiac (foregut), superior mesenteric (midgut), and inferior mesenteric (hindgut) arteries are maintained in the adult. However, the gut rotations and secondary retroperitoneal fixation of the ascending and descending colon produce a framing effect, whereby the colon tends to form a 3.5-sided frame about the small intestines. Half of the frame opening is usually between the sigmoid-rectal junction and the ileocecal junction. However, in Figure 3-1, which is a frontal view of an artist's three-dimensional rendering of the Visible Man's gastrointestinal tract and liver, we see what appears to be a full framing, with an unusual approximation of the cecum and the sigmoid colon. Within the general pattern of secondary mesenteric fixation, a wide range of clinically normative variation is seen. Pediatric, clinically significant anomalies are more commonly caused by failures in recanalization or innervation of the gut as well as by maldevelopment of the associated organs (i.e., pancreas, liver, appendix, and gall bladder). The stomach undergoes a different set of rotations and differential growth, maintaining dorsal mesenteric ligamentous connection to the liver anteriorly, the spleen posteriorly, and the transverse colon inferiorly. The greater omentum drapes a variable portion of the small intestines; however, it is not shown in Figure 3-1.

The first axial plate of this chapter depicts the upper end of the tenth thoracic vertebra. This level highlights the cardiac and the fundic portions of the stomach. The second plate shows the lower level of the same vertebra and presents the cardiac orifice and sphincter of the stomach. The body and antrum of the stomach are seen in the third and fourth plates.

Duodenum and adrenal glands are present in the fifth plate, which shows the upper portion of twelfth thoracic vertebra. The sixth plate shows the lower extent of this vertebra, the formation of the portal vein from the superior mesenteric vein,

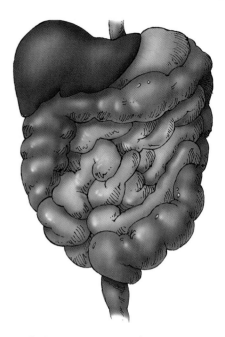

FIGURE 3-1 **Gastrointestinal Tract.** Embryological gut rotations and secondary fixation of the colon tend to leave it forming a 3.5-sided picture frame of the small intestines. Liver, red; stomach, light green; small intestine, middle green; large intestine, dark green.

and a variably present vein that proximally receives the inferior mesenteric and splenic veins. Taken at the base of the twelfth thoracic vertebra, the seventh plate presents the celiac artery. A view of the first lumbar vertebra at which the roof superior mesenteric artery can be seen exiting the descending aorta in close approximation to the celiac artery is depicted in the eighth plate. The closeness of these two arteries is common, even in large individuals such as the Visible Man. The ninth plate shows a more caudal transection of the first lumbar vertebra, presenting more of the superior mesenteric artery and the third part (horizontal) of the duodenum.

The tenth plate is at the level of the intervertebral disc between the first and the second lumbar vertebrae. Here we see much of the lateral course of the renal vessels. In the eleventh plate, this same intervertebral disc is viewed more inferiorly, and the head of the pancreas is seen to surround the major duodenal papilla. The twelfth plate is taken at the cranial portion of the second lumbar vertebra and presents the hilus of the left kidney. The thirteenth plate, taken through the caudal second lumbar, presents the duodenojejunal junction and the inferior portions of the kidneys.

A pass through the upper part of the third lumbar vertebra is shown in the fourteenth plate. The anteroinferiorly sloping rib cage has fully given over to the now clearly visualized oblique muscles. Similarly, the psoas muscles posteriorly indicate an area between the rib cage and the pelvis. The fifteenth plate depicts a pass through the fourth lumbar vertebra. The transition in layering of the oblique muscle aponeuroses making up the rectus sheath is apparent. The sixteenth plate, a view taken through the intervertebral disc between the fourth and the fifth vertebra, presents the superiormost iliac crests and formation of the inferior vena cava.

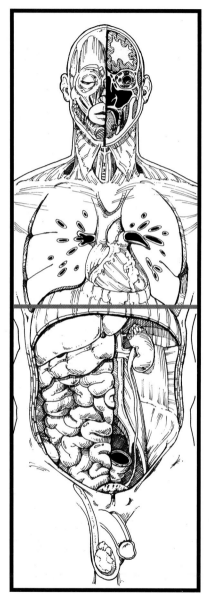

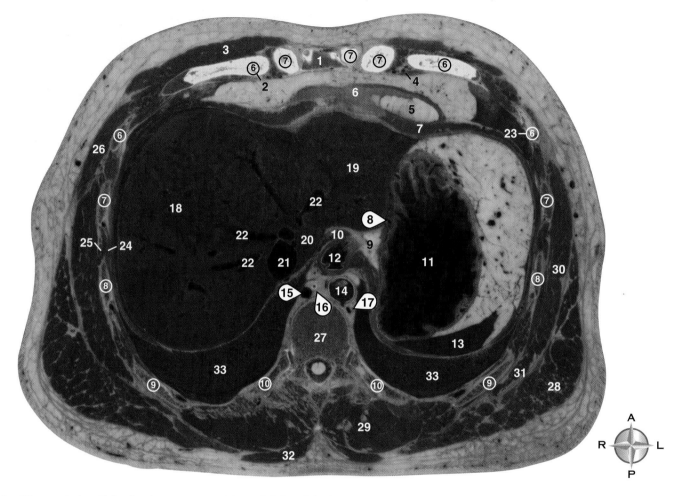

1 Sternum	
2 Costal cartilage (corresponding rib numbers are within circles)	
3 Rectus abdominis muscle	
4 Superior epigastric vessels	

5 Fibrous pericardial reflection	**19** Left lobe of the liver
6 Serous pericardium	**20** Caudate lobe of the liver
7 Diaphragm	**21** Inferior vena cava
8 Left gastric artery	**22** Hepatic vein
9 Gastrohepatic ligament	**23** Rib (corresponding rib numbers are within circles)
10 Lesser omentum	**24** Internal intercostal muscle
11 Fundus of the stomach	**25** External intercostal muscle
12 Esophagus	**26** Serratus anterior muscle
13 Spleen	**27** Tenth thoracic vertebra
14 Descending aorta	**28** Latissimus dorsi muscle
15 Azygos vein	**29** Erector spinae muscle
16 Thoracic duct	**30** External oblique muscle
17 Hemizygos vein	**31** Serratus posterior inferior muscle
18 Right lobe of the liver	**32** Trapezius muscle
	33 Inferior lobe of the lung

RADIOGRAPHIC KEY

a Linea alba
b Falciform ligament
c Linea semilunares
d Greater omentum
e Spinal cord
f Metastatic tumor growth
g Pancreas
h Pancreatic tumor
i Stomach
j Duodenum

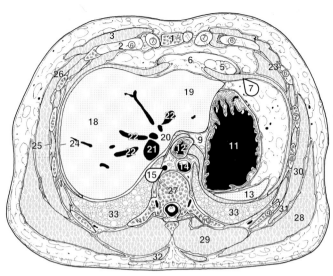

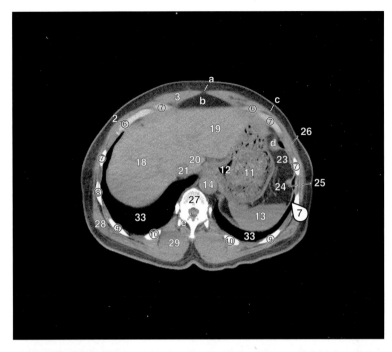

Corresponding CT. Section that also passes through the tenth thoracic vertebra. This patient also presents a large fatty mesenteric region, mostly formed by the greater omentum, which is mostly oriented toward the lateral surface of this portion of the stomach. However, patients rarely show as large a vacant stomach cavity as seen in the cryosection image. It is difficult to discern the hepatic veins and inferior vena cava on this normal CT image since no intravenous contrast was given.

Cryosection. The plane of the tenth thoracic vertebra characteristically intersects the passage of the esophagus through the diaphragm. The rugae of the stomach are prominent. The cardiac and fundic regions of the stomach are likely to be cranial to this level within the relatively lower left hemidiaphragmatic dome. It is relatively lower than the right hemidiaphragmatic dome that is situated over the liver. Anteriorly, the pericardial membranes extend inferiorly into the costodiaphragmatic space. The gastrohepatic ligament can be seen spanning the stomach and porta hepatis. It continues as lesser omentum into the left arm of the porta hepatis where the falciform ligament is found. Note the transverse course of the hepatic veins as this is the level at which they characteristically drain to the inferior vena cava.

Diagnostic Image. Thick-slice (10-mm) CT image is also at the level of the tenth thoracic vertebra. This patient presents an enlarged left lobe of the liver with several tumor masses.

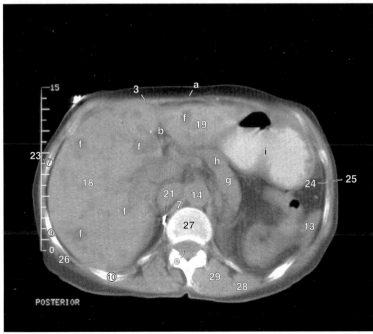

PLATE 3-2 ESOPHAGEAL SPHINCTER AND CARDIAC REGION STOMACH *(Visible Man 1508)*

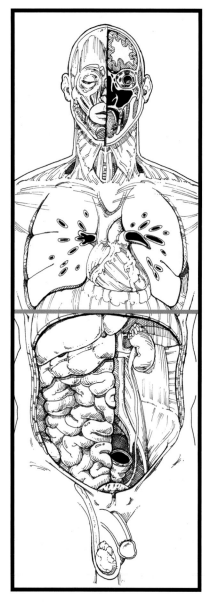

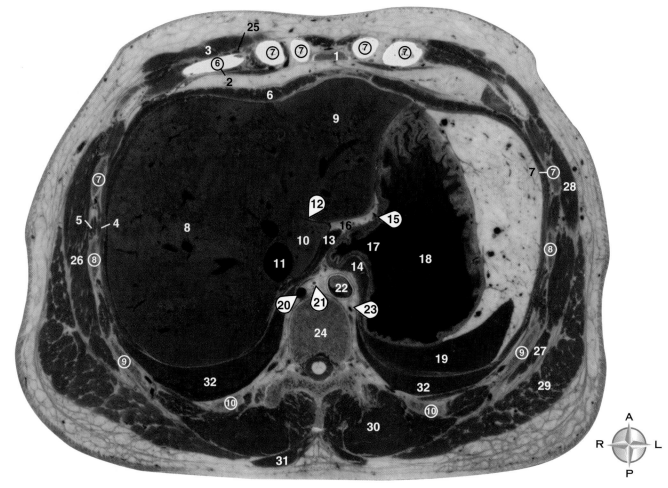

5 External intercostal muscle
6 Diaphragm
7 Rib (corresponding rib numbers are within circles)
8 Right lobe of the liver
9 Left lobe of the liver
10 Caudate lobe of the liver
11 Inferior vena cava
12 Falciform ligament
13 Right crus of the diaphragm
14 Left crus of the diaphragm
15 Left gastric vessels
16 Lesser omentum

17 Cardiac portion of the stomach
18 Body of the stomach
19 Spleen
20 Azygos vein
21 Thoracic duct
22 Descending aorta
23 Hemizygos vein
24 Tenth thoracic vertebra
25 Superior epigastric vessels
26 External oblique muscle
27 Serratus posterior inferior muscle
28 Serratus anterior muscle

29 Latissimus dorsi muscle
30 Erector spinae muscle
31 Trapezius muscle
32 Inferior lobe of the lung

RADIOGRAPHIC KEY

a Espophagus
b Linea alba
c Linea semilunares
d Greater omentum
T Thoracic vertebrae followed by the corresponding number

1 Xiphoid process
2 Costal cartilage (corresponding rib numbers are within circles)
3 Rectus abdominis muscle
4 Internal intercostal muscle

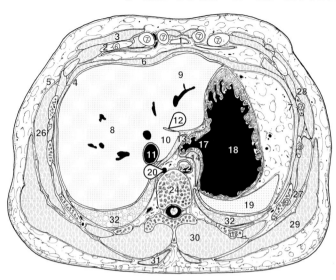

Corresponding CT. Section also at the level of the tenth thoracic vertebra. The inferior vena cava usually passes through the diaphragm at this level. The posterior surface of these vessels is highlighted; however, it is difficult to distinguish its anterior boundary or any of its hepatic vein tributaries. The full stomach is normal. The ventral mesentery of the liver (falciform ligament) is visible anterior to the liver at the midline. This level is commonly the maximum extent for the inspired lungs laterally. However, posteriorly, this is the level of the uninspired lungs with the twelfth thoracic vertebra (and the diaphragm) marking their maximum extent during full inspiration.

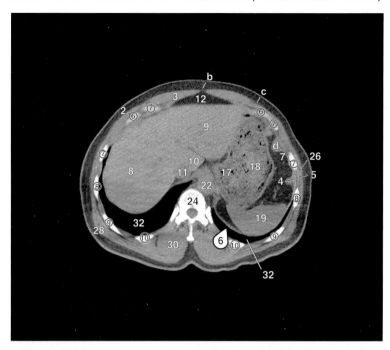

Cryosection. Cardiac orifice of the stomach, seen in a plane at the inferior portion of thoracic vertebral level T10, just inferior to the diaphragmatic covering of the esophageal sphincter seen in plate 3-1. The left and the right crura of the diaphragm are seen. Note the interleaving of the serratus anterior and external oblique muscles. The large fatty region surrounding the thoracic duct is likely to be the cisterna chyli, which is usually found anterior to the twelfth thoracic vertebra.

Diagnostic Image. Barium study of the distal esophagus near its junction with the stomach. The esophagus is distended with air and coated with swallowed barium. Note how the mucosal lining of the esophagus is demonstrated.

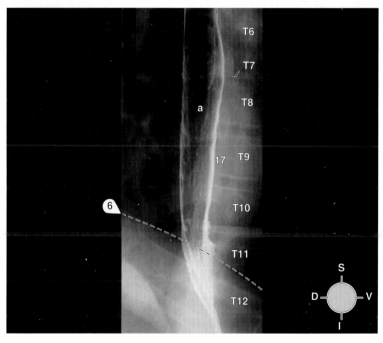

PLATE 3-3 INFERIORMOST DIAPHRAGM AND CELIAC STRUCTURES *(Visible Man 1553)*

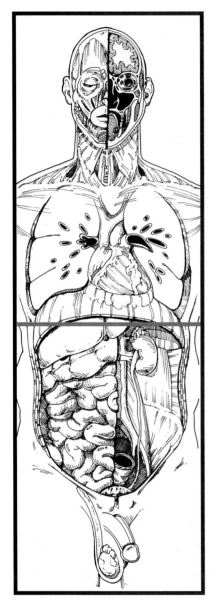

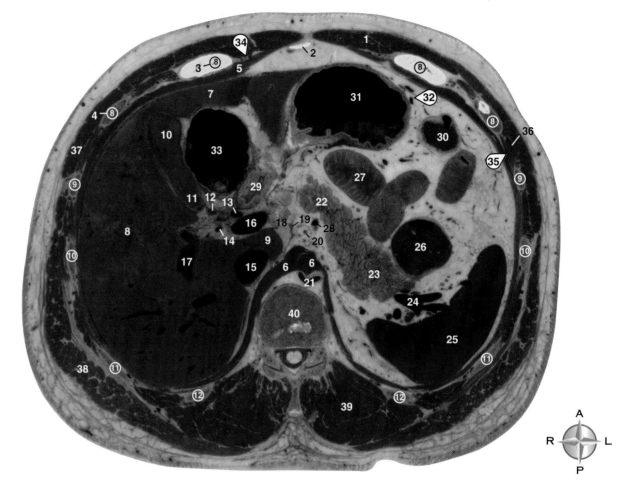

5	Diaphragm
6	Crus of the diaphragm
7	Left lobe of the liver
8	Right lobe of the liver
9	Caudate lobe of the liver
10	Body of the gall bladder
11	Neck of the gall bladder
12	Cystic duct
13	Common hepatic bile duct
14	Proper hepatic artery
15	Inferior vena cava
16	Portal vein
17	Hepatic vein
18	Celiac plexus
19	Celiac artery

20	Thoracic duct
21	Descending aorta
22	Body of the pancreas
23	Tail of the pancreas
24	Splenic vein
25	Spleen
26	Splenic flexure of the colon
27	Jejunum portion of the small intestine
28	Gastroduodenal artery
29	Superior portion of the duodenum
30	Transverse colon
31	Body of the stomach
32	Right gastrohepatic vessels
33	Hepatic flexure of the colon
34	Superior epigastric vessels

35	Internal intercostal muscle
36	External intercostal muscle
37	External oblique muscle
38	Latissimus dorsi muscle
39	Erector spinae muscle
40	Twelfth thoracic vertebra

RADIOGRAPHIC KEY

a	Linea alba
b	Linea semilunares
c	Greater omentum
d	Falciform ligament
e	Kidney
f	Descending portion of the duodenum
g	Gall bladder

1 Rectus abdominis muscle
2 Xiphoid process
3 Costal cartilage (corresponding rib numbers are within circles)
4 Rib (corresponding rib numbers are within circles)

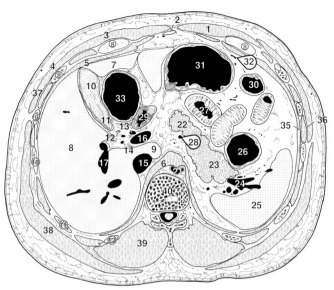

Corresponding CT. Section that also passes through the twelfth thoracic vertebra. This is commonly the level at which the aorta slips under the diaphragm. It is the most inferior structure to transition from the thorax to the abdomen. Also seen here, as is most commonly the case, the portal vein enters the liver just anterior to the inferior vena cava. Note that more of the pancreas is present in this section than in the cryosection.

Cryosection. Tail of the pancreas sits superior to the body at the level of the upper twelfth thoracic vertebra in the Visible Man. This level is just superior to the pyloric sphincter separating the stomach from the first part of the duodenum. The roof of the superior part of the duodenum is seen here. The structures of the portal triad (portal vein, common bile duct, proper hepatic artery) that sit within the lesser omentum are also apparent. The ascending and descending colon are labeled as flexure points, although these are actually somewhat superior. The one portion of colon labeled transverse colon, along with the artists' rendering, indicates that the transverse colon is descending from left to right, underneath the liver, in the Visible Man.

Diagnostic Image. Sagittal ultrasound image of the liver (directional key: S, superior; I, inferior; V, ventral; and D, dorsal). The inferior vena cava is clearly visualized on the posterior abdominal wall. The middle hepatic vein is seen, which, along with the gallbladder fossa, defines a plane that separates the right and left lobes of the liver. The ultrasound is obtained sagitally along this plane.

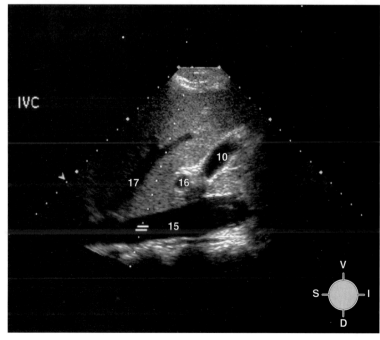

33

PLATE 3-4 PYLORIC SPHINCTER *(Visible Man 1562)*

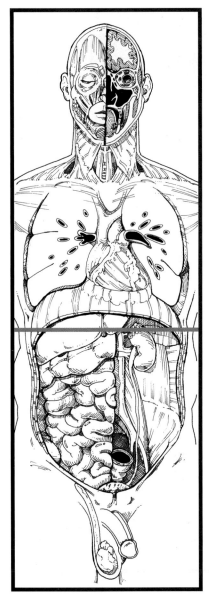

1 Rectus abdominis muscle
2 Xiphoid process
3 Costal cartilage (corresponding rib numbers are within circles)
4 Rib (corresponding rib numbers are within circles)
5 External intercostal muscle
6 Internal intercostal muscle
7 Intercostal artery
8 External oblique muscle
9 Crus of the diaphragm
10 Right lobe of the liver
11 Left lobe of the liver
12 Body of the gall bladder
13 Transverse colon
14 Body of the stomach
15 Antrum of the stomach
16 Pyloric sphincter
17 Cystic duct
18 Common bile duct
19 Proper hepatic artery
20 Descending colon
21 Jejunum portion of the small intestine
22 Duodenum portion of the small intestine
23 Body of the pancreas
24 Tail of the pancreas
25 Hepatic artery
26 Portal vein
27 Inferior vena cava
28 Hepatic vein
29 Splenic vein
30 Splenic artery
31 Spleen
32 Greater omentum
33 Right gastroepiploic vessels
34 Gastroduodenal vessels
35 Thoracic duct
36 Descending aorta

37 Suprarenal gland
38 Kidney
39 Perirenal fat
40 Twelfth thoracic vertebra
41 Erector spinae muscle
42 Latissimus dorsi muscle
43 Celiac artery

c Greater omentum
d Falciform ligament
e Hepatic flexure of the colon
f Splenic flexure of the colon
g Right hepatic bile duct
h Left hepatic bile duct
i Common hepatic bile duct
j Pancreatic duct
k Renal pelvis

RADIOGRAPHIC KEY

a Linea alba
b Linea semilunares

34

PLATE 3-4 PYLORIC SPHINCTER *(Visible Man 1562)*

Corresponding CT. Plane that also transects the twelfth thoracic vertebra. The aorta is now primarily through the diaphragmatic crura. The celiac artery can be seen emerging from its anterior surface. The hepatic reflection of the colon occurs at this level. Although it occurs somewhat cranial to this level, the ascending and transverse colon on either side are labeled as the splenic flexure. The suprarenal glands are visible on both sides, highlighted by surrounding fatty and areolar tissue. Although the base of the suprarenal glands may sit precisely on the cranial pole of the kidneys, their apices are often oriented anteriorly. Note the presence, location, and amount of air in the body of the stomach of this supine patient.

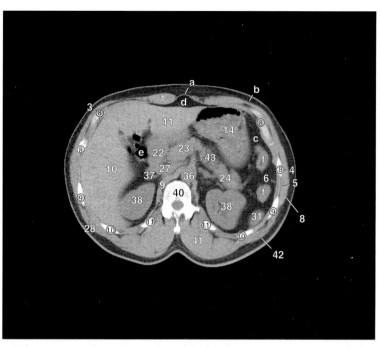

Cryosection. At the level of the twelfth thoracic vertebra, the antral and pyloric sphincter quickly transit to the superior portion of the duodenum in the Visible Man. The three structures in the portal triad (common bile duct, portal vein, and proper hepatic artery) are seen within the margin of the gastrohepatic ligament. The left suprarenal gland is seen anterior to the superior pole of the left kidney. The superior pole of the right suprarenal gland is also in view.

Diagnostic Image. MR cholangiogram is a technique to show the biliary tree without intervention or intravenous contrast. The technique causes fluid such as bile to be bright. Note the common bile duct and thin pancreatic duct. Urine in the right renal pelvis also turns bright. (Key: S, superior; L, left; I, inferior; R, right.)

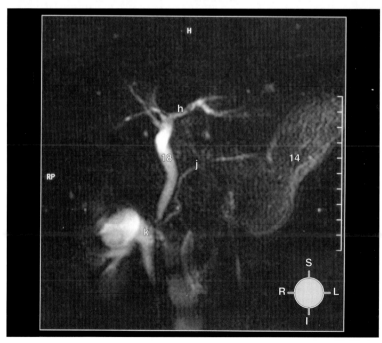

PLATE 3-5 SUPRARENAL GLANDS *(Visible Man 1570)*

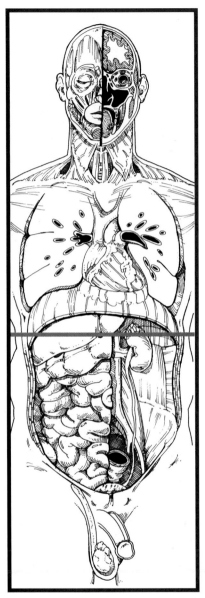

1 Rectus abdominis muscle
2 Linea alba
3 Costal cartilage
4 Rib (corresponding rib numbers are within circles)
5 External oblique muscle
6 Transversus abdominis muscle
7 External intercostal muscle
8 Internal intercostal muscle
9 Body of the stomach
10 Pyloric sphincter
11 Ascending colon
12 Transverse colon
13 Greater omentum
14 Descending colon
15 Ileum portion of the small intestine
16 Jejunum portion of the small intestine
17 Right lobe of the liver
18 Duodenum (descending portion)
19 Duodenaljejunal junction
20 Gastroduodenal vessels
21 Fundus of the gallbladder
22 Pancreas
23 Thoracic duct
24 Cystic duct
25 Common bile duct
26 Splenic artery
27 Portal vein
28 Hepatic flexure of the colon
29 Spleen
30 Splenic vein
31 Left suprarenal gland
32 Kidney
33 Intercostal artery
34 Descending aorta

35 Celiac artery
36 Right suprarenal gland
37 Inferior vena cava
38 Hepatic vein
39 Twelfth thoracic vertebra
40 Erector spinae muscle
41 Latissimus dorsi muscle
42 Falciform ligament

RADIOGRAPHIC KEY

a Linea alba
b Linea semilunares
c Greater omentum
d Falciform ligament
e Hepatic flexure of the colon
f Splenic flexure of the colon

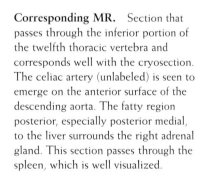

PLATE 3-5 SUPRARENAL GLANDS *(Visible Man 1570)*

Corresponding CT. Presence of the right kidney and the inferior pole of the spleen indicates that this cross section is somewhat inferior to the cryosection and corresponding magnetic resonance (MR) images. This plane transects the top of the body of L1 and the spinous process of T12. The superior mesenteric artery is seen to emerge from the descending aorta and ride under the pancreas. The pancreas is well visualized left and right of the superior mesenteric artery.

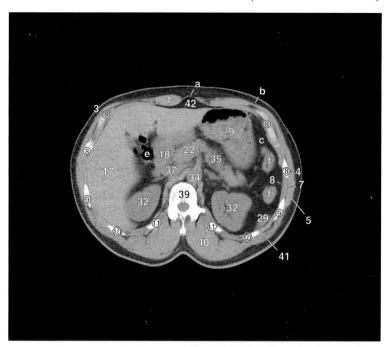

Cryosection. This section passes through the inferior portion of the twelfth thoracic vertebra. Both adrenal glands are seen. The descending portion of the duodenum is to the right of the head of the pancreas, whereas the duodenojejunal junction is appressed by the left side of the head of the pancreas. Much of the transverse colon is present at this level. The celiac artery is passing superiorly, anterior to its origin underneath the diaphragm on the anterior surface of the descending aorta. This section passes midway through the spleen, which is well visualized.

Corresponding MR. Section that passes through the inferior portion of the twelfth thoracic vertebra and corresponds well with the cryosection. The celiac artery (unlabeled) is seen to emerge on the anterior surface of the descending aorta. The fatty region posterior, especially posterior medial, to the liver surrounds the right adrenal gland. This section passes through the spleen, which is well visualized.

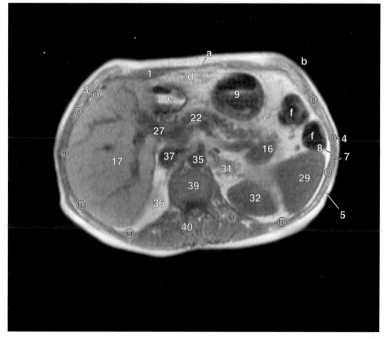

PLATE 3-6 FORMATION OF PORTAL VEIN *(Visible Man 1579)*

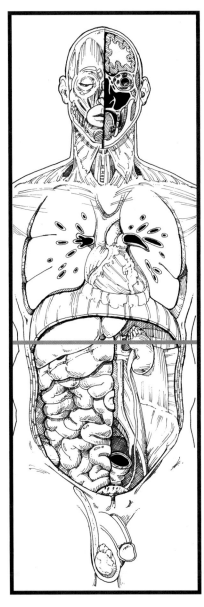

1 Linea alba
2 Rectus abdominis muscle
3 Superior epigastric vessels
4 Linea semilunares
5 External oblique muscle
6 Transversus abdominis muscle
7 Costal cartilage
8 External intercostal muscle
9 Internal intercostal muscle
10 Rib (corresponding
   rib numbers are
   within circles)
11 Ileocolic artery
12 Transverse colon
13 Body of the
   gallbladder
14 Right lobe of the liver
15 Ileum portion of the
   small intestine
16 Jejunum portion
   of the small intestine
17 Ascending colon
18 Descending colon
19 Greater omentum
20 Spleen
21 Kidney
22 Cortex of the kidney
23 Renal pyramids
24 Minor calyx of the kidney
25 Perirenal fat
26 Suprarenal gland
27 Splenic vein
28 Head of the pancreas
29 Descending portion
   of the duodenum
30 Inferior mesenteric vein
31 Descending aorta
32 First lumbar artery
33 Celiac artery
34 Superior mesenteric and portal
   vein merge

35 Inferior vena cava
36 Intervertebral disc between the
   twelfth thoracic and the first
   lumbar vertebrae
37 Erector spinae muscle
38 Latissimus dorsi muscle
39 Falciform ligament
40 First lumbar artery
41 Crus of the diaphragm

RADIOGRAPHIC KEY

a Renal vein
b Stomach
c Superior mesenteric vein
d Portal vein
e Right portal vein branch
f Left portal vein branch
g Superior mesenteric artery
h Body of pancreas

38

PLATE 3-6 FORMATION OF PORTAL VEIN (*Visible Man 1579*)

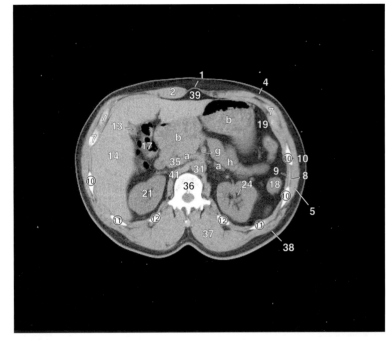

Corresponding CT. Plane passing inferior to the cryosection, through the top of the first lumbar vertebra. The base of the superior mesenteric artery is seen to emerge from the descending aorta. Note the long left renal vein seen crossing underneath the superior mesenteric artery.

Cryosection. The intervertebral disc between the twelfth thoracic and the first lumbar vertebrae of the Visible Man is the level at which the splenic and the inferior mesenteric veins often merge into a common trunk. This unnamed and variable anastomosis crosses the midline to join the superior mesenteric vein at this same level, and thus form the portal vein. The roof of the celiac artery is seen to emerge from the anterior descending aorta at this level in the Visible Man. It passes cranially after its emergence. Kidney substructures (i.e., the cortex, the calyces, and the pyramids) are visible at this level in the higher left kidney.

Diagnostic Image. Coronal MR angiogram that shows vasculature in the chest and abdomen. Note the formation of the portal vein from the superior mesenteric and splenic veins.

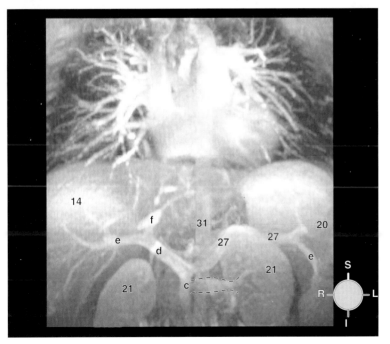

PLATE 3-7 CELIAC ARTERY *(Visible Man 1582)*

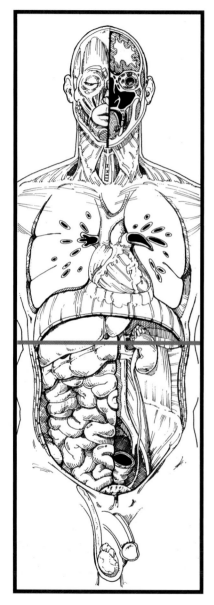

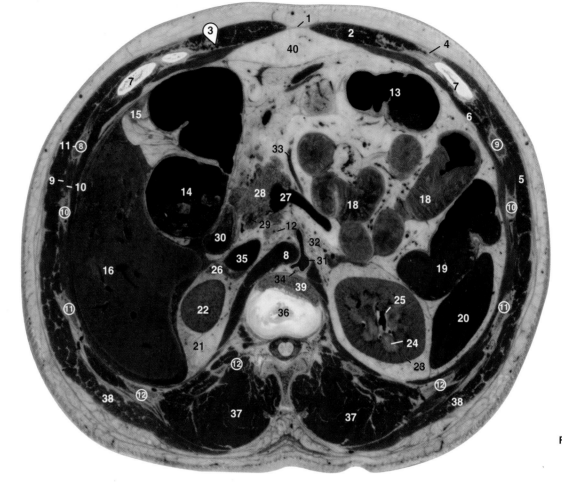

7   Costal cartilage
8   Crus of the diaphragm
9   External intercostal muscle
10 Internal intercostal muscle
11 Rib (corresponding rib numbers are within circles)
12 Ileocolic artery
13 Transverse colon
14 Ascending colon
15 Body of the gallbladder
16 Right lobe of the liver
17 Ileum portion of the small intestine
18 Jejunum portion of the small intestine
19 Descending colon
20 Spleen
21 Perirenal fat
22 Kidney

23 Cortex of the kidney
24 Renal pyramids
25 Minor calyx of the kidney
26 Suprarenal gland
27 Union of the superior and the inferior mesenterics, and splenic veins
28 Pancreas
29 Common bile duct
30 Descending portion of the duodenum
31 Descending aorta
32 Celiac artery
33 Superior mesenteric artery
34 First lumbar artery
35 Inferior vena cava
36 Intervertebral disk between the twelfth thoracic and the first lumbar vertebrae
37 Erector spinae muscle

38 Latissimus dorsi muscle
39 First lumbar vertebra
40 Falciform ligament

RADIOGRAPHIC KEY

a   Portal vein
b   Branches of portal vein
c   Superior mesenteric vein
d   Splenic vein
e   Inferior mesenteric vein
f   Left renal vein
g   Left common iliac artery
h   Right common iliac artery
i   Left common iliac vein
j   Right common iliac vein
k   Stomach

1   Linea alba
2   Rectus abdominis muscle
3   Superior epigastric vessels
4   Linea semilunares
5   External oblique muscle
6   Transversus abdominis muscle

40

PLATE 3-7 CELIAC ARTERY *(Visible Man 1582)*

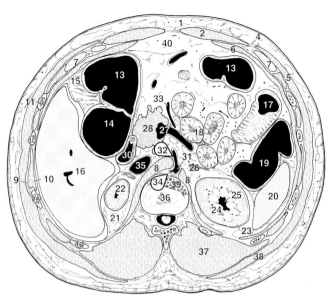

Corresponding CT. A plane through the lower portion of the first lumbar vertebra. However, this individual's stomach descends further than in the Visible Man. The superior mesenteric artery is seen descending within the small bowel mesentery, having arisen more superiorly.

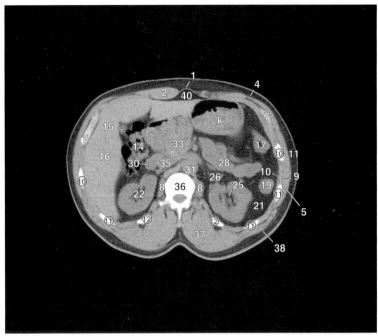

Cryosection. This section passes through the superiormost portion of the first lumbar vertebra of the Visible Man. The base of the celiac artery is seen to emerge anteriorly from the descending aorta before looping superiorly (see Plates 3-5 and 3-6). In most individuals this artery emerges under the median arcuate ligament of the diaphragm anterior to the twelfth thoracic vertebra. The top of the superior mesenteric artery is visible anterior to the structures joining to form the portal vein (i.e., superior mesenteric and splenic veins). It passes upward from a more inferior origin (see Plates 3-8 and 3-9).

Diagnostic Image. Coronal MR angiogram demonstrating abdominal venous anatomy. In this individual the inferior mesenteric vein can be seen joining the superior mesenteric vein. As their common trunk proceeds superiorly, it is joined by the splenic vein to produce the portal vein. Hepatic veins entering the inferior vena cava are seen. The left renal vein can be seen crossing anteriorly over the descending aorta. Both renal veins can be seen retrieving blood from large intersegmental veins within the kidneys. (Key: S, superior; L, left; I, inferior; R, right.)

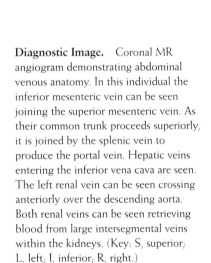

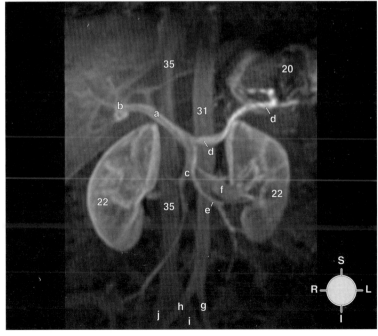

PLATE 3-8 SUPERIOR KIDNEYS (Visible Man 1590)

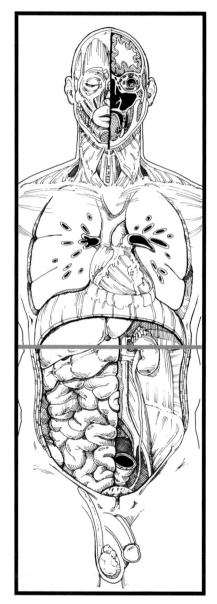

A
R ⊕ L
P

7   Costal cartilage (corresponding rib
    numbers are within circles)
8   Crus of the diaphragm
9   External intercostal muscle
10 Internal intercostal muscle
11 Rib (corresponding rib numbers are
    within circles)
12 Ileocolic artery
13 Transverse colon
14 Ascending colon
15 Right lobe of the liver
16 Jejunum portion of the small intestine
17 Jejunal branches of the mesenteric vessels
18 Descending colon
19 Spleen

20 Head of the pancreas
21 Common bile duct
22 Perirenal fat
23 Intrarenal fat
24 Kidney
25 Cortex of the kidney
26 Major calyx of the kidney
27 Minor calyx of the kidney
28 Renal pyramid
29 Renal pelvis
30 Descending portion of the duodenum
31 Descending aorta
32 First lumbar artery
33 Superior mesenteric vein
34 Superior mesenteric artery

35 Inferior vena cava
36 First lumbar vertebra
37 Erector spinae muscle
38 Latissimus dorsi muscle
39 Falciform ligament

RADIOGRAPHIC KEY

a   Left renal artery
b   Left renal vein
c   Right renal vein
d   Right renal artery
e   Gallbladder
f   Infarct
g   Nodes
h   Stomach

1   Linea alba
2   Rectus abdominis muscle
3   Linea semilunares
4   Inferior epigastric vessels
5   External oblique muscle
6   Transversus abdominis muscle

PLATE 3-8 SUPERIOR KIDNEYS *(Visible Man 1590)*

Corresponding CT. Section that also passes through the lower portion of the first lumbar vertebra. Much of the transverse colon can be seen in this level. The superior mesenteric artery is seen to lie directly on top of the aorta. The left renal vessels are found at this level, whereas they are found superior to this level in the Visible Man.

Cryosection. This section passes through the lower first lumbar vertebra. Two minor calyces can be seen to drain into a major, which finds its way into the renal pelvis. The roof of the superior mesenteric artery, as it emerges from the anterior surface of the descending aorta, is seen. Perirenal fat around hilar structures is seen within the left kidney. Pararenal fat is seen to encase both kidneys.

Diagnostic Image. CT Section that passes through the upper portion of the second lumbar vertebra. The radiopaque dye in this contrast study highlights the descending aorta, renal arteries, and kidneys. However, a nonenhancing portion of the kidney (labeled "f") represents an infarct. Enlarged lymph nodes around the inferior vena cava and descending aorta are noted.

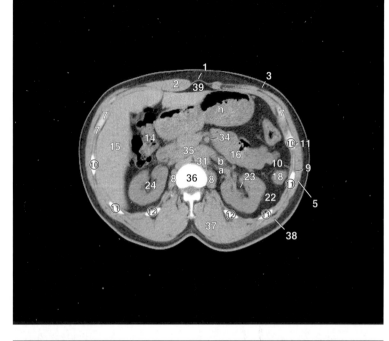

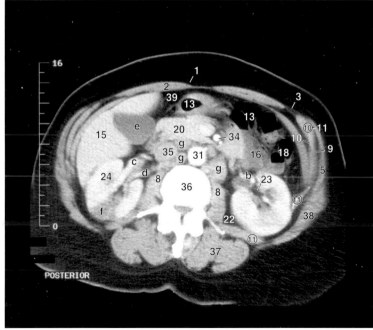

PLATE 3-9 SUPERIOR MESENTERIC ARTERY *(Visible Man 1601)*

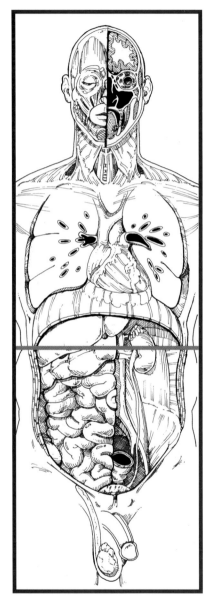

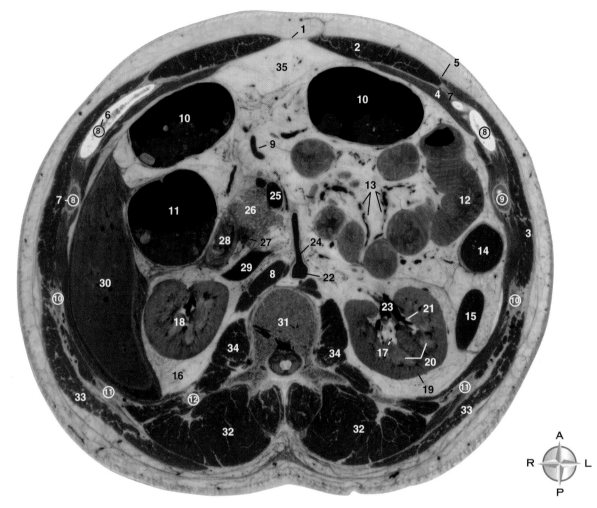

7   Rib (corresponding rib numbers are within circles)
8   Crus of the diaphragm
9   Ileocolic artery
10 Transverse colon
11 Ascending colon
12 Jejunum portion of the small intestine
13 Jejunal branches of the mesenteric vessels
14 Descending colon
15 Spleen
16 Perirenal fat
17 Intrarenal fat
18 Kidney
19 Cortex of the kidney
20 Renal pyramid

21 Major calyx of the kidney
22 Descending aorta
23 Renal hilus
24 Superior mesenteric artery
25 Superior mesenteric vein
26 Head of the pancreas
27 Common bile duct
28 Descending portion of the duodenum
29 Inferior vena cava
30 Right lobe of the liver
31 First lumbar vertebra
32 Erector spinae muscle
33 Latissimus dorsi muscle
34 Psoas major muscle
35 Falciform ligament

RADIOGRAPHIC KEY

a   Stomach
b   Left renal artery
c   Right renal artery
d   Pulmonary artery
e   Common iliac artery
f   Internal iliac artery
g   External iliac artery
h   Inferior mesenteric artery
i   Right renal vein
j   Left renal vein
k   Splenic artery
l   Celiac trunk
m   Pancreas

1   Linea alba
2   Rectus abdominis muscle
3   External oblique muscle
4   Transversus abdominis muscle
5   Linea semilunares
6   Costal cartilage (corresponding rib numbers are within circles)

44

PLATE 3-9 SUPERIOR MESENTERIC ARTERY *(Visible Man 1601)*

Corresponding CT. Section that also passes through the lower first lumbar vertebra. Jejunal sections of the small intestine are seen. The right renal vein and the left renal artery are seen passing through both renal hila.

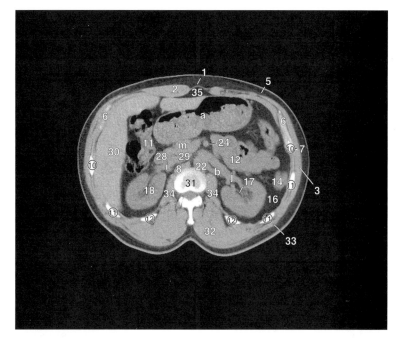

Cryosection. This section passes through the lower first lumbar vertebra. From its origin, the superior mesenteric artery passes under the pancreas and into the mesentery of the small intestine. The long horizontal path over the third, or horizontal, part of the duodenum is an important radiological landmark. The left renal pelvis and most cranial portion of the psoas major muscle are seen at this level.

Diagnostic Image. MR angiogram showing a coronal view of the abdominal vessels. The MR angiogram is obtained immediately after injection of contrast. Note the enhancement of the kidneys as the contrast reaches the renal arterial system. Note the mesenteric arteries and aortic bifurcation. (Key: S, superior; L, left; I, inferior; R, right.)

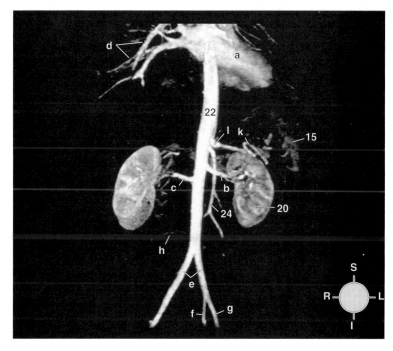

PLATE 3-10 HILUS OF KIDNEY: RENAL VEINS *(Visible Man 1610)*

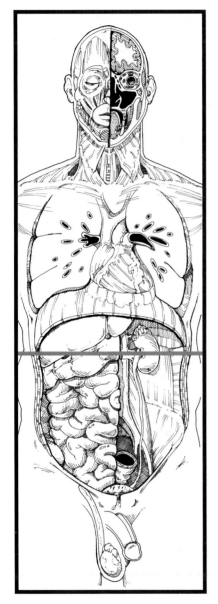

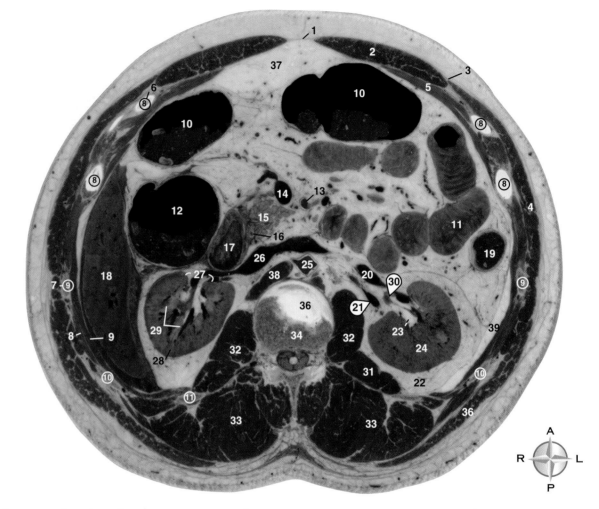

7   Rib (corresponding rib numbers are within circles)
8   External intercostal muscle
9   Internal intercostal muscle
10 Transverse colon
11 Jejunum portion of the small intestine
12 Ascending colon
13 Superior mesenteric artery
14 Superior mesenteric vein
15 Head of the pancreas
16 Common bile duct
17 Descending portion of the duodenum
18 Right lobe of the liver
19 Descending colon

20 Renal vein
21 Renal artery
22 Perirenal fat
23 Intrarenal fat
24 Kidney
25 Descending aorta
26 Inferior vena cava
27 Renal pelvis
28 Cortex of the kidney
29 Renal pyramid
30 Ureter
31 Quadratus lumborum muscle
32 Psoas major muscle
33 Erector spinae muscle

34 First lumbar vertebra
35 Intervertebral disk between the first and the second lumbar vertebrae
36 Latissimus dorsi muscle
37 Falciform ligament
38 Crus of the diaphragm
39 Pararenal fat

RADIOGRAPHIC KEY

a   Jejunum portion of the small intestine
b   Splenic vein
c   Body of pancreac
d   Left lobe of liver
e   Stomach

1   Linea alba
2   Rectus abdominis muscle
3   Linea semilunares
4   External oblique muscle
5   Transversus abdominis muscle
6   Costal cartilage (corresponding rib numbers are within circles)

PLATE 3-10 HILUS OF KIDNEY: RENAL VEINS *(Visible Man 1610)*

Corresponding CT. Section that also passes through the inferiormost portion of the first lumbar vertebra and likely the intervertebral disk between the first and the second lumbar vertebrae. It is similar to the corresponding CT image in Plate 3-9, however, more of the renal vessels are present as well as the left ureter.

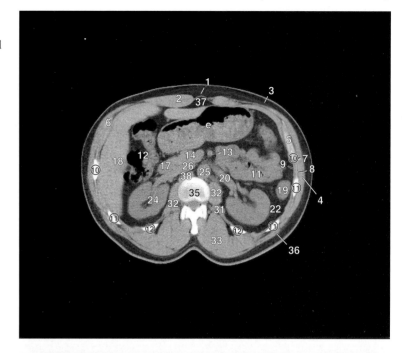

Cryosection. This section passes through the inferiormost first lumbar vertebra and intervertebral disc between the first and second lumbar vertebrae. The superiormost part of the right kidney hilus and an area lower in the left kidney hilus are both highlighted by perirenal fat. The right and left renal veins both drain to the inferior vena cava at this level. A portion of the left renal artery that fills a gap in Visible Man slice 1615 is seen as is the emergence of the right renal artery. An intermesenteric branch of the superior mesenteric artery that is likely supplying the superiormost jejunum and ileum is seen next to the superior mesenteric vein. The main trunk of the superior mesenteric artery emerged from the anterior surface of the descending aorta superior to this level (see Visible Man 1601).

Diagnostic Image. Ultrasound section passes through the inferior portion of the first lumbar vertebra. It is an axial ultrasound image taken with the transducer positioned on the anterior midline of the abdominal wall. The left renal vein is seen. The inferior vena cava and the descending aorta are also seen posteriorly. The superior mesenteric artery and vein are seen anteriorly. The position of the pancreas and its relationship to the splenic vein and superior mesenteric artery and vein are demonstrated. (Key: A, anterior; L, left; P, posterior; R, right.)

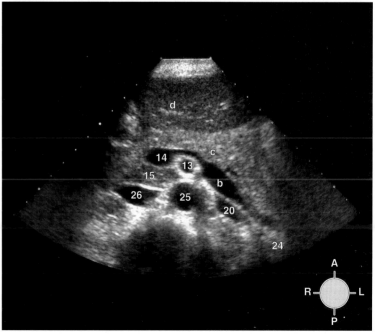

47

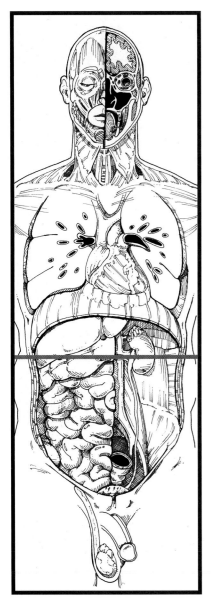

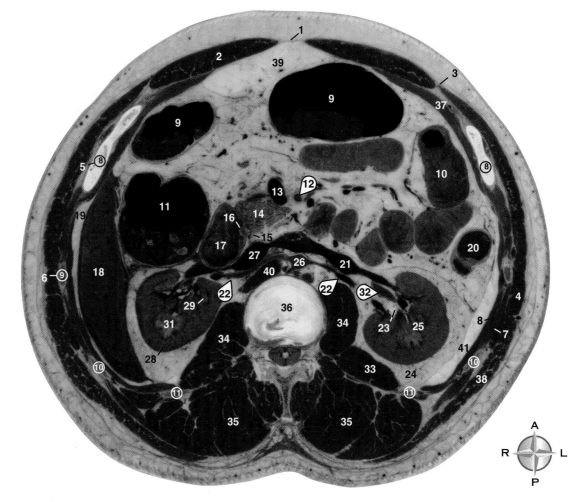

1   Linea alba
2   Rectus abdominis muscle
3   Linea semilunares
4   External oblique muscle
5   Costal cartilage (corresponding rib numbers are within circles)

6   Rib (corresponding rib numbers are within circles)
7   External intercostal muscle
8   Internal intercostal muscle
9   Transverse colon
10 Jejunum portion of the small intestine
11 Ascending colon
12 Superior mesenteric artery
13 Superior mesenteric vein
14 Head of the pancreas
15 Pancreatic duct
16 Major duodenal papilla
17 Descending portion of the duodenum
18 Right lobe of the liver
19 Fatty peritoneal lining

20 Descending colon
21 Renal vein
22 Renal artery
23 Intrarenal fat
24 Perirenal fat
25 Kidney
26 Descending aorta
27 Inferior vena cava
28 Cortex of the kidney
29 Minor calyx of the kidney
30 Major calyx of the kidney
31 Renal pyramids
32 Ureter
33 Quadratus lumborum muscle

34 Psoas major muscle
35 Erector spinae muscle
36 Intervertebral disk between the first and the second lumbar vertebrae
37 Transversus abdominis muscle
38 Latissimus dorsi muscle
39 Falciform ligament
40 Crus of the diaphragm
41 Pararenal fat

RADIOGRAPHIC KEY

a   Stomach
b   Right portal vein
c   Spleen

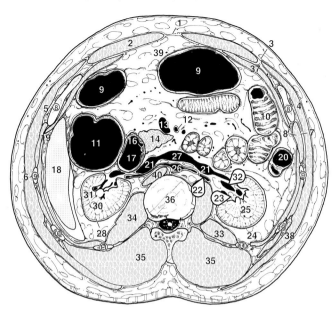

Corresponding CT. This section passes through the superiormost portion of the second lumbar vertebra. This image is similar to the corresponding CT image in Plate 3-10, however, the greater radiodensity of the vertebral body and the full view of the L1/L2 zygapophyses (posterior articular processes) indicate that this plane cuts more inferiorly through the second lumbar vertebra. Portions of the renal arteries and veins are seen to be directly associated with the aorta and the inferior vena cava. The cranialmost quadratus lumborum muscle is present.

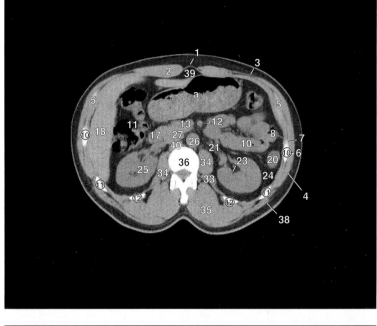

Cryosection. This section passes through the center of the intervertebral disc between the first and the second lumbar vertebrae. There is a trace of the first lumbar vertebral body, pedicles, and spinous process. The major duodenal papilla is seen to the right of the main pancreatic duct within the head of the pancreas. Lower portions of the superoinferiorly wide and anteroposteriorly flat renal veins present in Visible Man slice 1610 are present. The majority of both renal veins is visible. The roof of the left ureter is visible.

Corresponding MR. This section that passes through the first lumbar vertebrae somewhat superior to level seen in the cryosection image. This is demonstrated by the relative presence of more of the right lobe of the liver, the inferior pole of the spleen, and what appears to be a region above the hilus of the right kidney. However, this level also appears to be at the inferior extent of this individual's ribcage.

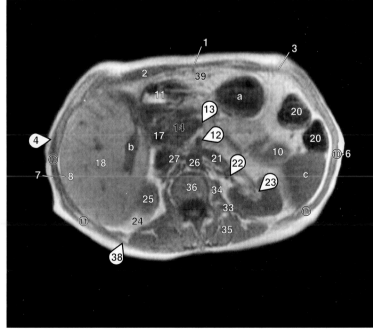

PLATE 3-12 HILUS OF KIDNEY: LEFT URETER *(Visible Man 1625)*

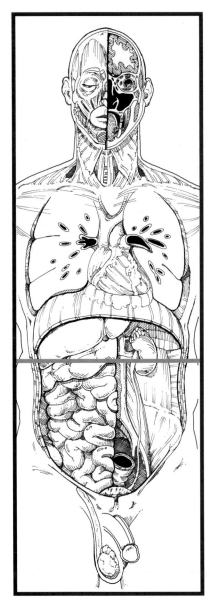

1 Linea alba
2 Rectus abdominis muscle
3 Linea semilunares
4 External oblique muscle
5 Internal oblique muscle
6 Transversus abdominis muscle
7 Rib (corresponding rib numbers are within circles)
8 External intercostal muscle
9 Internal intercostal muscle
10 Crus of the diaphragm
11 Transverse colon
12 Jejunum portion of the small intestine
13 Ascending colon
14 Terminal branches of the superior mesenteric artery
15 Superior mesenteric vein
16 Inferior mesenteric vein
17 Descending portion of the duodenum
18 Right lobe of the liver
19 Descending colon
20 Renal vein
21 Ureter
22 Intrarenal fat
23 Perirenal fat
24 Renal pelvis
25 Major calyx of the kidney
26 Kidney
27 Descending aorta
28 Cortex of the kidney
29 Quadratus lumborum muscle
30 Psoas major muscle
31 Erector spinae muscle
32 Inferior vena cava
33 Second lumbar vertebra
34 Spinous process of the first lumbar vertebra
35 Latissimus dorsi muscle
36 Falciform ligament
37 Pararenal fat

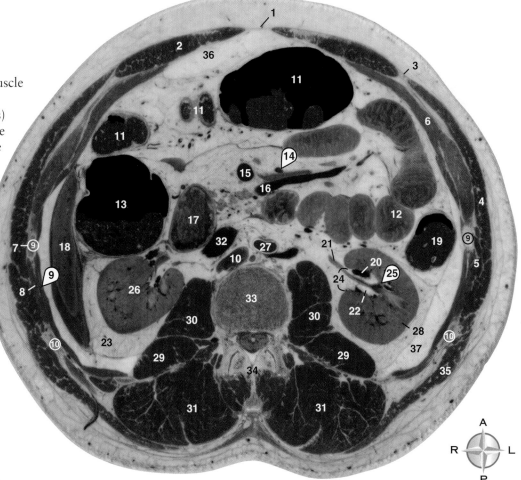

RADIOGRAPHIC KEY

a Stomach
b Minor calyx
c Sacrum
d Ilium
e Arcuate line of the ilium
f Pectineal line of the superior pubic ramus
g Pelvic inlet
h Superior pubic ramus

i Superior ischial ramus
j Bladder
k Sacroiliac joint
l Femoral head
m Femoral neck
n Acetabulum
L Lumbar vertebrae followed by the corresponding number
T Thoracic vertebrae followed by the corresponding number

PLATE 3-12 HILUS OF KIDNEY: LEFT URETER *(Visible Man 1625)*

Corresponding CT. This section also passes through the superiormost part of the second lumbar vertebra. This level is similar to Plate 3-11; however, the inferior position can be inferred by the discontinuities amongst the left renal vessels.

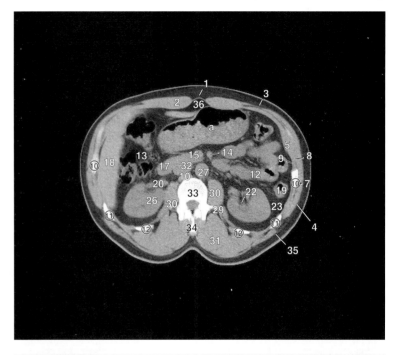

Cryosection. This section passes through the superiormost portion of the second lumbar vertebrae. The pedicles and spinous processes of the first lumbar vertebra are present posteriorly. Both layers of external oblique muscle aponeurosis contribute to the external rectus sheath. Note that the aponeurosis of the internal oblique muscle is split, with the external investing layer passing anteriorly in the rectus sheath and the inner investing layer passing posteriorly in the rectus sheath with the aponeurosis of transversus abdominis. A major calyx drains into the roof of the left renal pelvis, which is seen to continue as the left ureter.

Diagnostic Image. Coronal posterior-to-anterior plain-film pyelogram radiograph (directional key: S, superior; L, left; I, inferior; R, right). Dye in the urine highlights the renal calyces, renal pelvis, ureters, and bladder. Note that kidney on the left side is higher, as is usually the case. The position of the bladder in the pelvis is apparent.

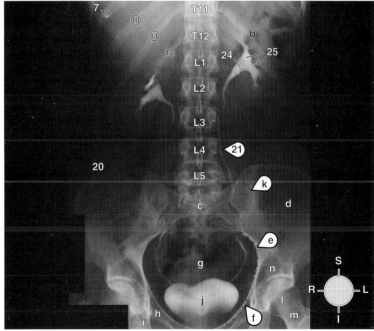

PLATE 3-13 INFERIOR KIDNEY AND DUODENOJEJUNAL JUNCTION *(Visible Man 1634)*

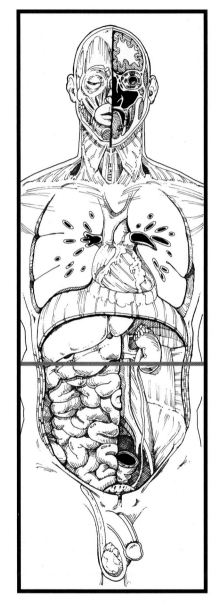

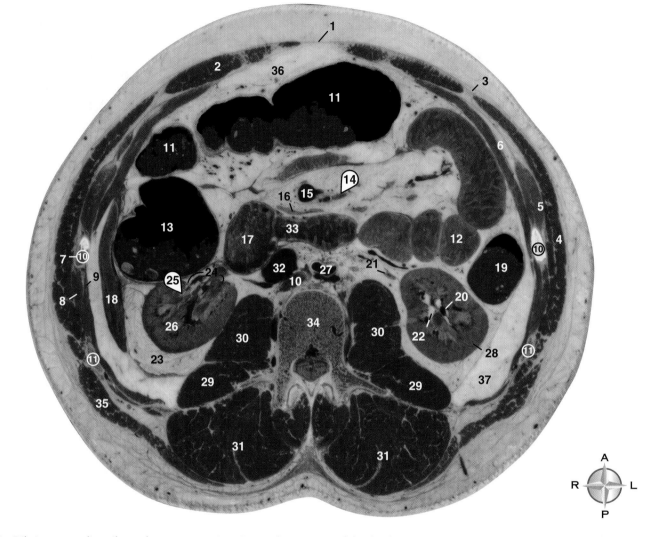

7 Rib (corresponding rib numbers are within circles)
8 External intercostal muscle
9 Internal intercostal muscle
10 Crus of the diaphragm
11 Transverse colon
12 Jejunum portion of the small intestine
13 Ascending colon
14 Terminal branches of the superior mesenteric artery
15 Superior mesenteric vein
16 Inferior mesenteric vein

17 Descending portion of the duodenum
18 Right lobe of the liver
19 Descending colon
20 Renal vein
21 Ureter
22 Intrarenal fat
23 Perirenal fat
24 Renal pelvis
25 Major calyx of the kidney
26 Kidney
27 Descending aorta
28 Cortex of the kidney

29 Quadratus lumborum muscle
30 Psoas major muscle
31 Erector spinae muscle
32 Inferior vena cava
33 Transverse portion of Duodenum
34 Second lumbar vertebra
35 Latissimus dorsi
36 Falciform ligament
37 Pararenal fat

RADIOGRAPHIC KEY

a Stomach

1 Linea alba
2 Rectus abdominis muscle
3 Linea semilunares
4 External oblique muscle
5 Internal oblique muscle
6 Transversus abdominis muscle

52

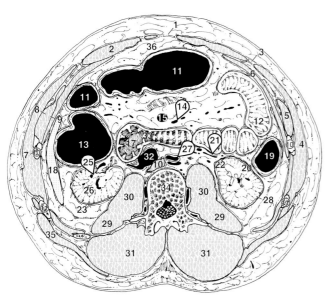

Cryosection. This section passes through the middle of the second lumbar vertebrae. The duodenojejunal junction is present at this level of the Visible Man.

Corresponding CT. This section also passes through the middle of the second lumbar vertebra. This level is similar to Plate 3-12.

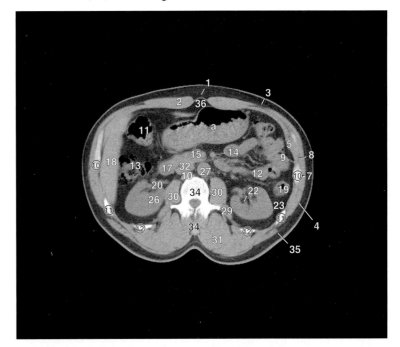

Diagnostic Image. A sagittal ultrasound of the right kidney and right lobe of the liver. Note how the liver parenchyma and kidney cortex appear similar. Note the brightness of the perirenal fat and the fat around the kidney. Note the psoas muscle posterior to the kidney. (Key: V, ventral; I, inferior; D, dorsal; S, superior.)

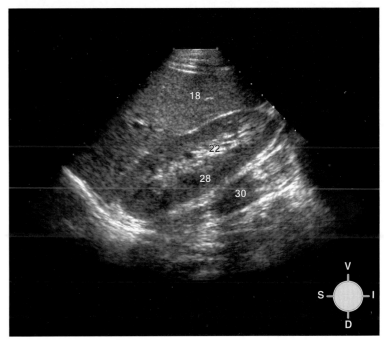

53

PLATE 3-14 LOWER ABDOMEN: OBLIQUE MUSCLES *(Visible Man 1700)*

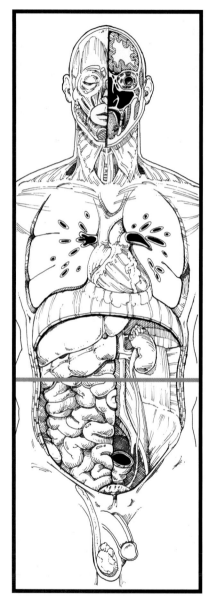

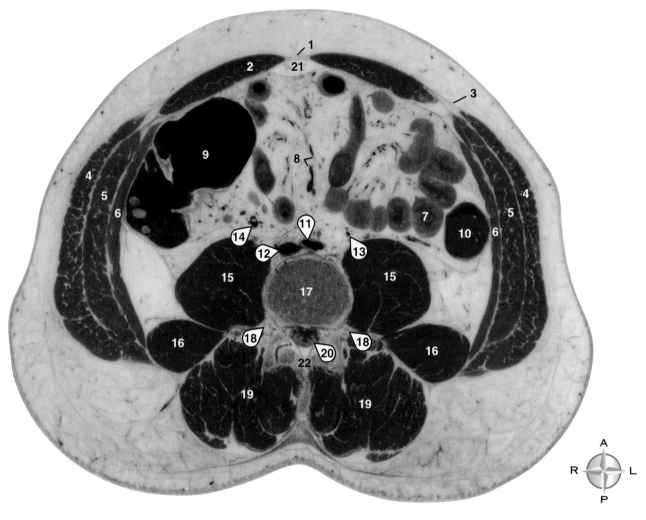

1	Linea alba	12	Inferior vena cava
2	Rectus abdominis muscle	13	Left ureter
3	Linea semilunares	14	Right ureter
4	External oblique muscle	15	Psoas major muscle
5	Internal oblique muscle	16	Quadratus lumborum muscle
6	Transversus abdominis muscle	17	Third lumbar vertebra
7	Jejunum	18	Ventral rami
8	Branches of the superior mesenteric artery	19	Erector spinae muscle
9	Ascending colon	20	Cauda equine
10	Descending colon	21	Falciform ligament
11	Descending aorta	22	Second lumbar vertebra

RADIOGRAPHIC KEY

a   Appendix
b   Ascending colon
c   Descending colon
d   Sigmoid colon
e   Rectum
f   Femoral head
g   Iliac blade
h   Femoral neck

PLATE 3-14 LOWER ABDOMEN: OBLIQUE MUSCLES *(Visible Man 1700)*

Corresponding CT. This section passes through the same level as in the cryosection image. The oblique muscles and their contributions to the rectus sheath are equally well differentiable.

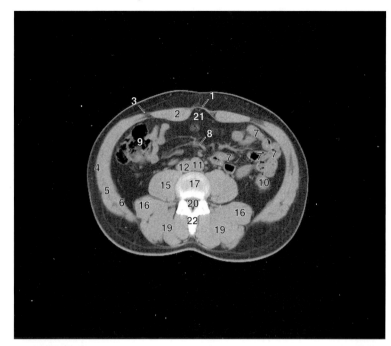

Cryosection. This section passes primarily through the upper part of the third lumbar vertebra. This is indicated by the posterior portion that presents the pedicles and spinous processes of the second lumbar vertebra. Between the third and the fourth lumbar vertebrae there are usually no ribs or pelvis, thus the abdominal organs are less protected here than they are superiorly or inferiorly. Fortunately, usually little or none of the kidneys is exposed at this level. Usually, the inferior mesenteric artery is seen branching from the descending aorta near this level; however, this appears not to be the case for the Visible Man. Note that the aponeurosis of the internal oblique muscle is split, with the external investing layer passing anteriorly in the rectus sheath and the inner investing layer passing posteriorly in the rectus sheath with the aponeurosis of transversus abdominis. Note the ventral rami that contribute significantly to the femoral nerve that forms within the psoas major muscle.

Diagnostic Image. Coronal plain-film radiograph taken posterior to anterior. Radiopaque barium dye was injected into the rectum (i.e., barium enema or lower gastrointestinal study). The sigmoid colon is somewhat elongated on this individual. It overlaps a superior cecum and appendix at the upper left of the image (the patient's right). Since the cecum is fully enhanced, the barium had reached this proximal most portion of the large bowel when this film was taken. (Key: S, superior; L, left; I, inferior; R, right.)

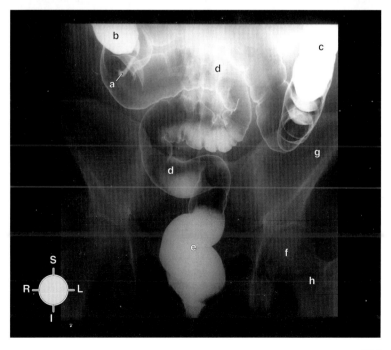

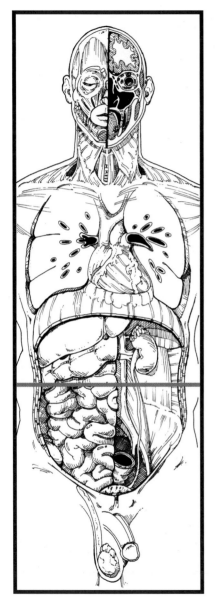

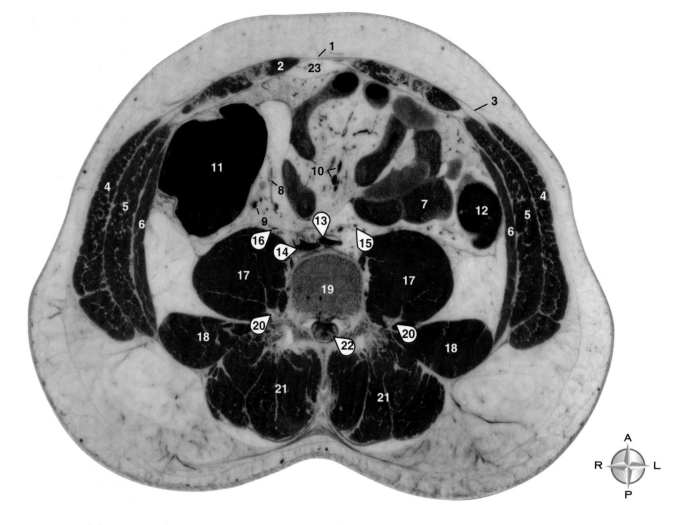

6 Transversus abdominis muscle
7 Ileum
8 Ileocolic artery
9 Ileocolic vein
10 Branches of the superior mesenteric artery
11 Ascending colon
12 Descending colon
13 Descending aorta
14 Inferior vena cava
15 Left ureter
16 Right ureter

1 Linea alba
2 Rectus abdominis muscle
3 Linea semilunares
4 External oblique muscle
5 Internal oblique muscle

17 Psoas major muscle
18 Quadratus lumborum muscle
19 Fourth lumbar vertebrae
20 Ventral rami
21 Erector spinae muscle
22 Cauda equine
23 Falciform ligament

RADIOGRAPHIC KEY

a Right common iliac artery
b Left common iliac artery

c Body of the stomach
d Antrum of the stomach
e Pyloric sphincter
f Superior portion of the duodenum
g Jejunum
h Rib (corresponding rib numbers are within circles)
T Thoracic vertebrae followed by the corresponding number
L Lumbar vertebrae followed by the corresponding number

PLATE 3-15 LOWER ABDOMEN: FOURTH LUMBAR VERTEBRAL LEVEL (Visible Man 1715)

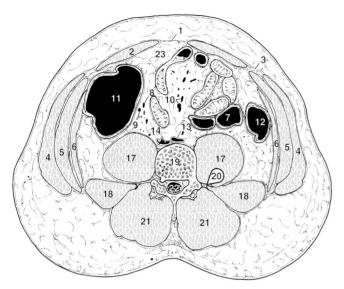

Cryosection. This section passes through the fourth lumbar vertebrae. As in Plate 3-14, the aponeurosis of the internal oblique muscle is split, with the external investing layer passing anteriorly in the rectus sheath and the inner investing layer passing posteriorly in the rectus sheath with the aponeurosis of transversus abdominis. Note the ventral rami that contribute significantly to the femoral nerve that forms within the psoas major muscle.

Corresponding CT. Same level as that in the cryosection. In this patient the aorta has already split into the common iliac arteries at this level.

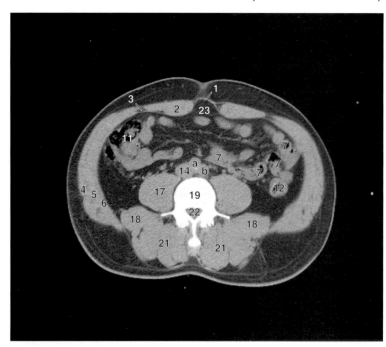

Diagnostic Image. Coronal plain-film radiograph taken posterior to anterior. Radiopaque barium dye was swallowed (i.e., barium swallow or upper gastrointestinal study). The body, antrum, and pyloric sphincter of the stomach are well visualized. Note that the small bowel is filled with barium. Note the normal "feathery" fold pattern of the jejunum and the more smooth contour of the ileum.

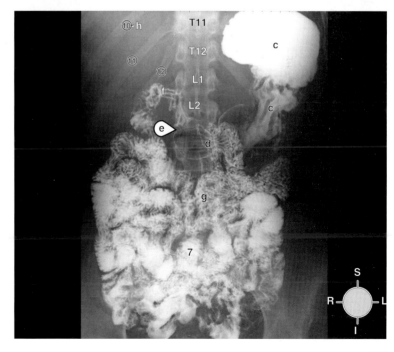

PLATE 3-16 LOWER ABDOMEN: ILIAC CRESTS *(Visible Man 1733)*

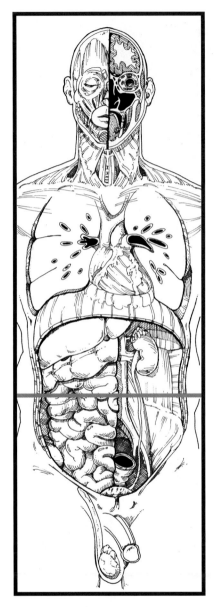

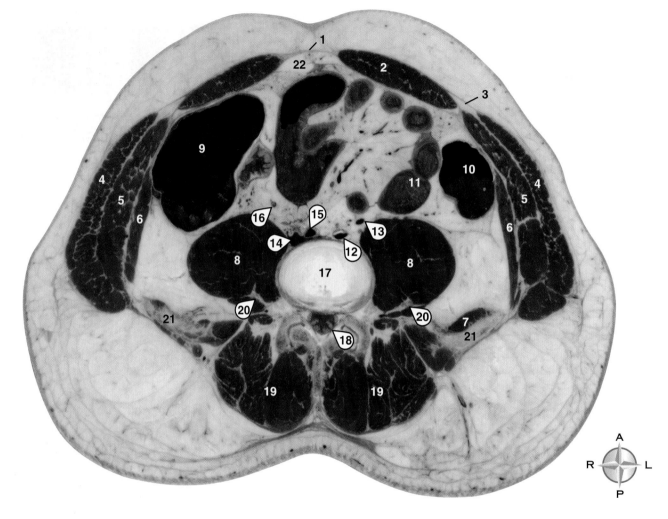

5 Internal oblique muscle
6 Transversus abdominis
7 Quadratus lumborum muscle
8 Psoas major muscle
9 Ascending colon
10 Descending colon
11 Ileum
12 Left common iliac artery
13 Left ureter
14 Inferior vena cava
15 Right common iliac artery

16 Right ureter
17 Intervertebral disk between the fourth and the fifth lumbar vertebrae
18 Cauda equine
19 Erector spinae muscle
20 Ventral rami
21 Iliac crest of the ilium
22 Falciform ligament

RADIOGRAPHIC KEY
a Body of the fifth lumbar vertebra

b Arch of the fourth lumbar vertebra
c Umbilicus
d Gas in the transverse colon
e Aortic aneurysm
f Catheter for injection of contrast
g Ilium portion of the pelvis
h External iliac artery
i Femoral artery
j Descending aorta
L Lumbar vertebrae followed by the corresponding number

1 Linea alba
2 Rectus abdominis muscle
3 Linea semilunares
4 External oblique muscle

58

PLATE 3-16 LOWER ABDOMEN: ILIAC CRESTS (Visible Man 1733)

Corresponding CT. Same level as that of the cryosection. The umbilicus is visible at this level. Within the umbilicus, the falciform ligament, carrying ligamentum teres (vestigial umbilical vein) enters the anterior abdominal wall superiorly, joining the urachus (vestigial fetal bladder), which enters inferiorly. Unlike the cryosection, none of the iliac crest is discernible.

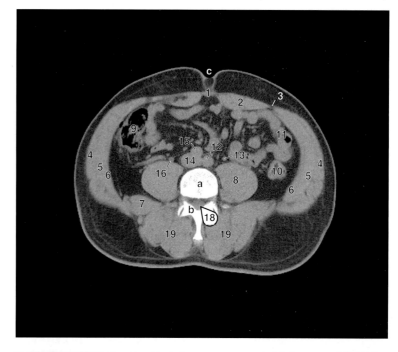

Cryosection. This section passes through the center of the intervertebral disc between the fourth and the fifth lumbar vertebrae. Also seen just posterior to the disk are the transverse processes and inferior zygapophyses (joint facets) of the fifth lumbar vertebra. On the posterior side of the fifth lumbar vertebra zygapophyses are those for the fourth lumbar vertebra. The quadratus lumborum muscle takes origin from the iliac crest on the posterior abdominal wall. The cranialmost portion of the iliac crest is visible. A small portion of the origin of the left quadratus lumborum muscle is visible. Note the presence of two common iliac arteries that indicate the splitting of the descending aorta superiorly, whereas the inferior vena cava receives the two common iliac veins inferiorly.

Diagnostic Image. Frontal film from an aortic angiogram. The catheter was placed percutaneously into the right femoral artery and advanced up into the aorta. Contrast was injected through the catheter to visualize the aorta and pelvic arteries. Note the abnormal enlargement of the upper and mid-abdominal aorta. (Key: S, superior; L, left; I, inferior; R, right.)

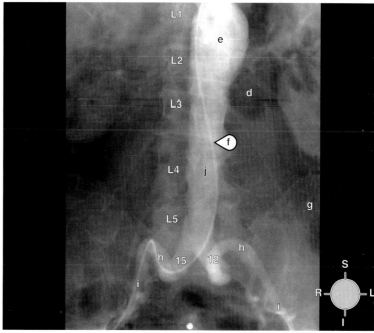

CHAPTER 4

Pelvis, Perineum, and External Genitalia

INTRODUCTION

The pelvis and perineum contain four sizeable compartments; from superior to inferior, they are the false pelvis, true pelvis, deep perineal space (or pouch), and the superficial perineal space (or pouch). The false pelvis is surrounded by the rectus sheath, oblique muscles, iliac blades, and lower lumbar spine. The true pelvis begins at the pelvic brim (sacral prominence, arcuate line, pectineal line) and ends at the pelvic outlet (ischiopubic ramus, ischial tuberosity, ischium, sacrum, coccyx).

The pelvic viscera, depending on their contents, distend from the urogenital diaphragm (pelvic floor) upward into the abdomen. The peritoneal sac extends inferiorly onto the top of these viscera, creating outpouchings anterior and posterior to the bladder, and, in females, around the uterus as well. The male and female retropubic and rectovesicle pouches are seen in Figures 4-1 and 4-2, respectively. The female rectouterine pouch is also seen.

The first Visible Man cryosection, Plate 4-1, of this chapter passes through the center of the fifth lumbar vertebra. The junction of the two common iliac veins into the inferior vena cava occurs at this level. The second Visible Man cryosection, Plate 4-2, passes through the first sacral vertebra and the sacroiliac joint. The descending aorta is seen to split into the common iliac arteries at this level. The two bellies of the iliopsoas (iliacus and

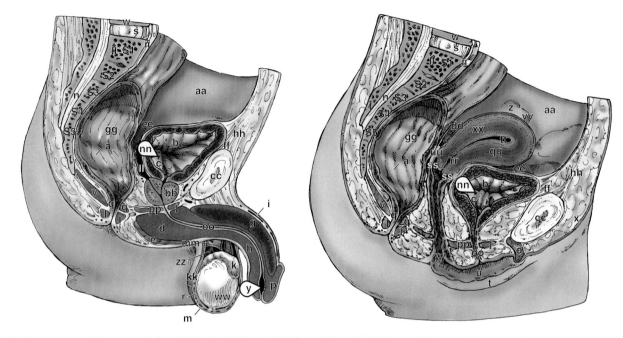

FIGURES 4-1 AND 4-2 Midsagittal View of Male and Female Pelvises. Undistended morphology and position of the pelvic viscera. Labeled structures: a, anal columns; b, bladder; c, bladder trigone; d, bulb of the penis (corpus spongiosum); e, bulbospongiosus muscle; f, coccygeal vertebrae (Co1-2); g, corpus cavernosum; h, corpus spongiosum; i, deep dorsal vein of penis; j, deep perineal pouch; k, epididymis; l, external anal sphincter muscle; m, external spermatic fascia; n, filum terminale; o, glans clitoris; p, glans penis; q, internal anal sphincter muscle; r, internal spermatic fascia; s, intervertebral disc (L5/S1); t, labia majora; u, labia minora; v, levator ani muscle; w, lumbar vertebra (L5); x, mons pubis; y, navicular fossa; z, ovary; aa, peritoneal cavity; bb, prostate gland; cc, pubic symphysis; dd, rectouterine pouch; ee, rectovesicle pouch; ff, retropubic space; gg, rectum; hh, rectus abdominis muscle; ii, sacral promontory; jj, sacral vertebrae (S1-5); kk, scrotal sac; ll, seminal vesicle; mm, spermatic cord; nn, ureter entry into trigone; oo, urethra; pp, urogenital (UG) diaphragm; qq, uterine body; rr, uterine cervix; ss, uterine fornices (posterior and anterior); tt, uterine fundus; uu, uterine os; vv, uterine (fallopian) tube; ww, tunica vaginalis; xx, uterus; yy, vagina; and zz, vas deferens.

psoas major) muscle are seen to come together bilaterally at this level. The third Visible Man cryosection, Plate 4-3, passes through the fifth sacral vertebra as well as the roof of the acetabulum. The femoral vessels and nerve are also seen to leave the pelvis at this level. The fourth Visible Man cryosection, Plate 4-4, passes through the inferior coccyx. The obturator canal and vessels and the intertrochanteric crest of the right and the left femora are seen here.

The male genitalia are in view in the remaining Visible Man cryosection images. The fifth Visible Man cryosection, Plate 4-5, passes through the superior pelvic outlet. The prostate gland and ejaculatory ducts are seen here. Both spermatic cords have also come into view, although the structures on the right are diminutive owing to an undescended testicle (i.e., only the left testicle is present in the Visible Man). The deep perineal pouch is seen in the sixth Visible Man cryosection,

Plate 4-6, which also passes through the ischiopubic ramus and femoral lesser trochanters. The seventh Visible Man cryosection, Plate 4-7, passes through the bulb of the penis and a more inferior portion of the femoral lesser trochanters. The eighth Visible Man cryosection, Plate 4-8, passes through the midshaft of the penis and the spermatic cord. It also passes through the femoral diaphysis below the lesser trochanters. The ninth Visible Man cryosection, Plate 4-9, passes through the testicle and the upper third of the femoral diaphysis.

The female sex organs are in view in the remaining cryosection images in this chapter, all of which derive from the Visible Woman data. Plate 4-10 is of a cryosection that passes through the uterus sitting within the true pelvis of the Visible Woman. It also intersects the fifth sacral vertebra, the ilial portion of the acetabulum, and the femoral head. Plate 4-11 is of a cryosection that passes through the cervix of the Visible Woman's uterus. Plate 4-12 shows a cryosection that passes through the fornices that ring the cervical os of the Visible Woman's uterus. Plate 4-13 is of a cryosection that passes through the deep pouch of the Visible Woman. The urethra and urethral sphincter are present. The mons pubis, overlying the pubic symphysis, is also visible externally. Plate 4-14 shows a cryosection that passes through the glans clitoris of the Visible Woman. The dorsal nerves, vessels, and erectile tissue are visible.

PLATE 4-1 SUPERIOR ILIAC CRESTS *(Visible Man 1749)*

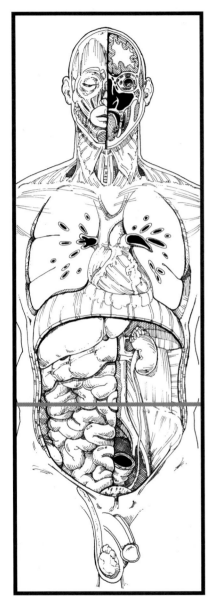

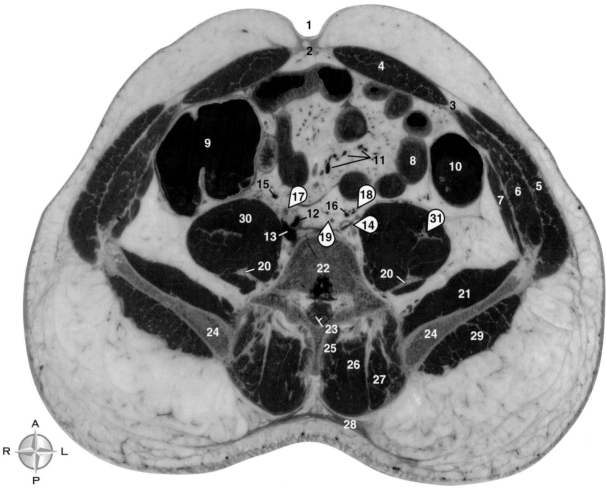

1	Umbilicus
2	Linea alba
3	Linea semilunares
4	Rectus abdominis muscle
5	External oblique muscle
6	Internal oblique muscle
7	Transversus abdominis muscle
8	Ileum portion of the small intestine
9	Ascending colon
10	Descending colon
11	Superior mesenteric arterial branches to ileum
12	Right common iliac artery
13	Inferior vena cava
14	Left common iliac artery
15	Right testicular vein
16	Left testicular vein
17	Right ureter
18	Left ureter
19	Superior rectal vessels
20	Ventral rami
21	Iliacus muscle
22	Fifth lumbar vertebra
23	Cauda equina
24	Iliac blade
25	Spinalis muscle
26	Longissimus muscle
27	Iliocostalis muscle
28	Thoracolumbar fascia
29	Gluteus medius muscle
30	Psoas major muscle
31	Femoral nerve

RADIOGRAPHIC KEY

a	Right common iliac vein
b	Left common iliac vein
c	Transverse colon
d	Ileocecal junction
e	Appendix
f	Rectum
g	Femoral head
L	Lumbar vertebrae followed by the corresponding number

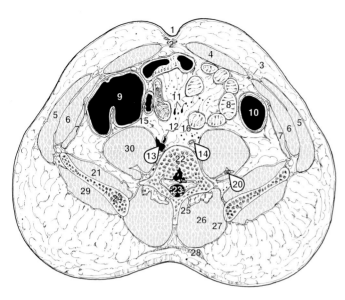

Cryosection. This section passes through the center of the fifth lumbar vertebra. Note that both fascial planes of the internal oblique pass anterior to the rectus sheath at this level. The pedicles, transverse processes and the superior articular facet of the fifth lumbar vertebra are robust owing to the weight and strain this region bears. The large marrow cavity of the iliac crest is apparent. The superior rectal vein has a portacaval anastomosis with the middle rectal vein. It is potentially involved in rectal hemorrhoids. Note that the origin of the inferior vena cava is somewhere between this plane and the next inferior (Visible Man, Plate 4-2, page 1805).

Corresponding Computed Tomography (CT). Section that matches that of the cryosection well. However, the aorta is in the process of splitting into the common iliac arteries, and the umbilicus is not present. The ascending and the descending portions of the colon are discernible from the mesentery-suspended ileum.

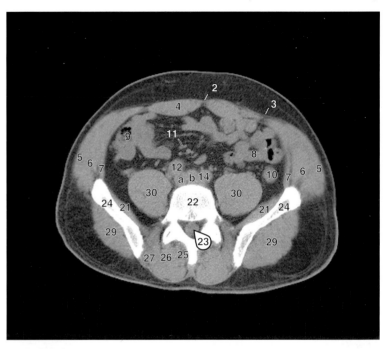

Diagnostic Image. An anterior-to-posterior plain-film radiograph taken after a barium enema was administered to the patient (directional key: S, superior; I, inferior; R, right; and L, left). Note that the barium has reached the ileocecal junction. It has also entered the vermiform appendix. Barium has collected at the base of the haustra of the transverse colon but has nearly evacuated from the sigmoid colon into the rectum. This person's colon is normal as is the fixation of their gut to the posterior abdominal wall. Despite its lack of clinical relevance, note that, compared with most anatomical texts, the ascending colon is fixed somewhat cranially and that the sigmoid colon must have a large mesentery and extends further to the right side than in most people.

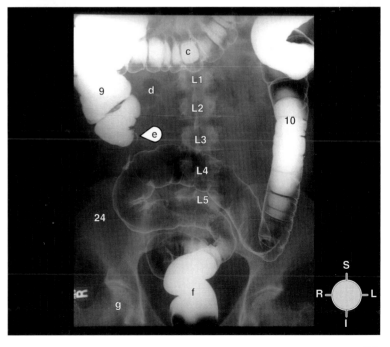

PLATE 4-2 SACROILIAC JOINT *(Visible Man 1805)*

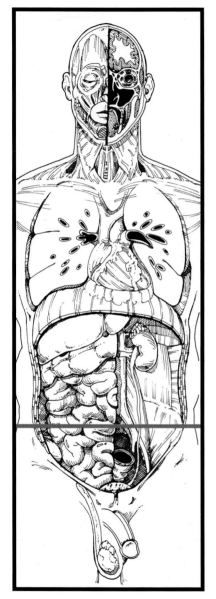

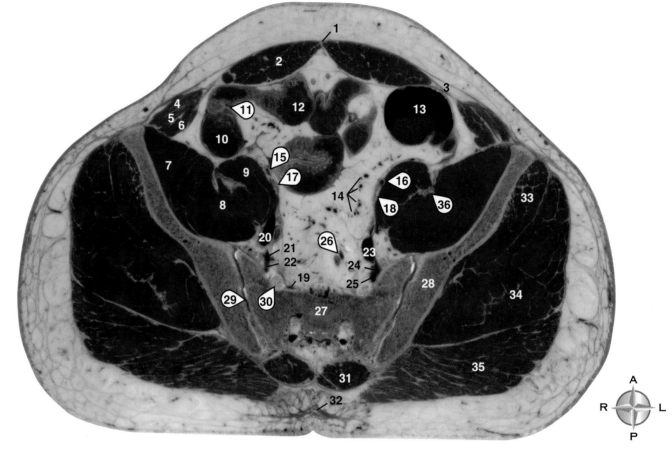

6 Transversus abdominis
   muscle
7 Iliacus muscle
8 Psoas major muscle
9 Iliopsoas muscle
10 Cecum
11 Ileocolic valve
12 Ileum portion of the
   small intestine
13 Descending colon
14 Superior mesenteric
   arterial branches to the
   ileum
15 Right ureter
16 Left ureter

17 Right external iliac artery
18 Left external iliac artery
19 Median sacral artery
20 Right common iliac vein
21 Right internal iliac vein
22 Right superior gluteal
   artery
23 Left common iliac vein
24 Left internal iliac artery
25 Left superior gluteal
   artery
26 Superior rectal vessels
27 First sacral vertebra
28 Iliac blade
29 Sacroiliac joint

30 Sacral nerve roots
31 Iliocostalis/longissimus
   muscles
32 Thoracolumbar fascia
33 Gluteus minimis muscle
34 Gluteus medius muscle
35 Gluteus maximus muscle
36 Femoral nerve

RADIOGRAPHIC KEY

a Rectum
b Ascending colon
c Transverse colon
d Hepatic flexure

e Splenic flexure
f Sigmoid colon
g Haustra
h Femoral head
i Right common iliac artery
j Left external iliac artery
   and vein
k Left internal iliac artery
   and vein
L Lumbar vertebrae
   followed by the
   corresponding number
T Thoracic vertebrae
   followed by the
   corresponding number

1 Linea alba
2 Rectus abdominis muscle
3 Linea semilunares
4 External oblique muscle
5 Internal oblique muscle

PLATE 4-2 SACROILIAC JOINT *(Visible Man 1805)*

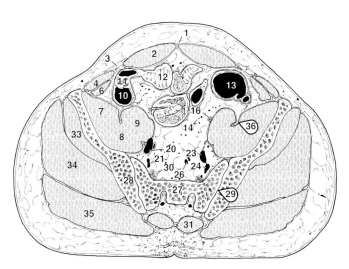

Corresponding CT. Also a section through the first sacral vertebra. Although both images are male, this individual's hips are noticeably narrower than those of the Visible Man.

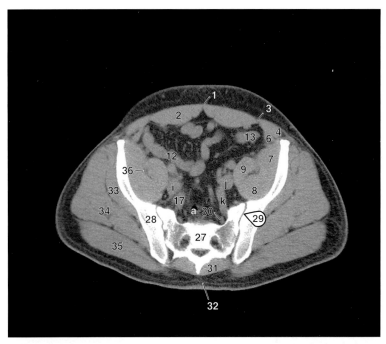

Cryosection. This section passes through the center of the first sacral vertebra. Both oblique muscles and transversus abdominis contribute their entire fascial covering to the anterior leaf of the rectus sheath, leaving the internal surface covered by a much weaker fascia than that found superiorly. The common iliac artery has bifurcated at this level, whereas the roots of the common iliac vein are further inferior. The base of the ileocecal valve is seen at this level. The iliopsoas is seen as a single body forming from the psoas major and iliacus muscles. It is a hip flexor, or, if the hip is stationary, it is a powerful trunk flexor. The largest muscle in the body, gluteus maximus is present posteriorly. Note the large and coarse muscle fibers.

Diagnostic Image. An anterior-to-posterior plain-film x-ray taken after a barium enema was administered to the patient (directional key: A, superior; P, inferior; R, right; and L, left). Note that the barium has reached the ileocecal junction; however, in Plate 4-1, it has not highlighted the vermiform appendix. Barium fills the transverse colon but has nearly evacuated from the rest of the colon and rectum. The splenic flexure is usually found higher than the hepatic flexure. Note the narrowing of the splenic flexure with thumb-like impressions along the wall of the colon. The appearance is due to Crohn's disease, an inflammatory disease of the bowel.

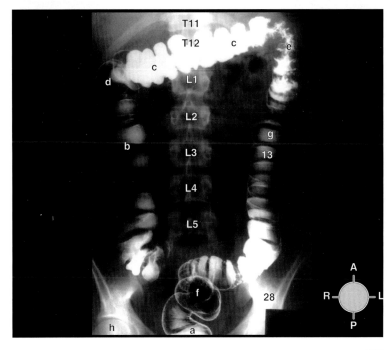

65

PLATE 4-3 SUPERIOR BLADDER AND ACETABULUM (*Visible Man 1880*)

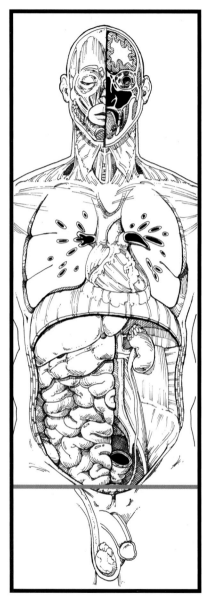

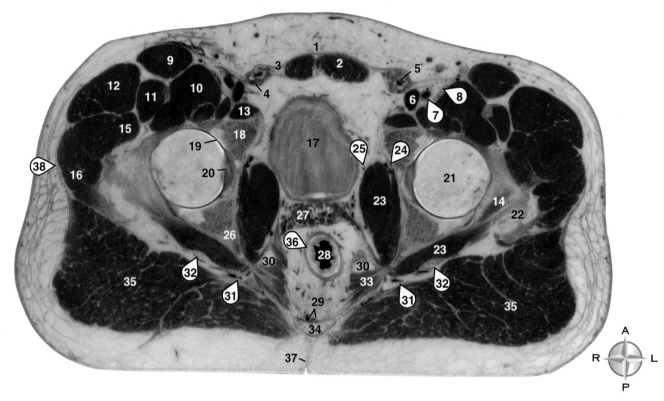

1	Linea alba	17	Urinary bladder	32	Sciatic nerve
2	Rectus abdominis muscle	18	Pubis	33	Levator ani muscle
3	Linea semilunares	19	Acetabulum	34	Fifth sacral vertebra
4	Spermatic cord	20	Ligamentum teres	35	Gluteus maximus muscle
5	Vas deferens	21	Head of the femur	36	External muscular coat of the rectum
6	Femoral vein	22	Greater trochanter of the femur	37	Cluneal groove
7	Femoral artery	23	Medial and lateral portions of the obturator internus muscle	38	Iliotibial tract
8	Femoral nerve	24	Obturator vessels		
9	Sartorius muscle	25	Obturator nerve		

1 Linea alba
2 Rectus abdominis muscle
3 Linea semilunares
4 Spermatic cord
5 Vas deferens
6 Femoral vein
7 Femoral artery
8 Femoral nerve
9 Sartorius muscle
10 Iliopsoas muscle
11 Rectus femoris muscle
12 Tensor fascia lata muscle
13 Pectineus muscle
14 Ilium
15 Gluteus minimis muscle
16 Gluteus medius muscle

17 Urinary bladder
18 Pubis
19 Acetabulum
20 Ligamentum teres
21 Head of the femur
22 Greater trochanter of the femur
23 Medial and lateral portions of the obturator internus muscle
24 Obturator vessels
25 Obturator nerve
26 Ischial spine
27 Seminal vesicles
28 Rectum
29 Superior rectal vessels
30 Ischiorectal fossa
31 Inferior gluteal vessels

32 Sciatic nerve
33 Levator ani muscle
34 Fifth sacral vertebra
35 Gluteus maximus muscle
36 External muscular coat of the rectum
37 Cluneal groove
38 Iliotibial tract

RADIOGRAPHIC KEY

a Lymph node
b Prostate
c Urethra (catheter)
d Radioactive seeds
e Second sacral vertebra

PLATE 4-3 SUPERIOR BLADDER AND ACETABULUM *(Visible Man 1880)*

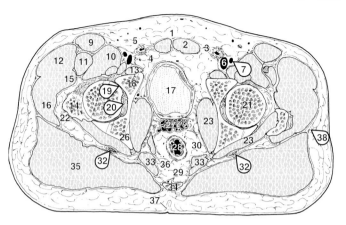

Corresponding CT. Section that passes through the second sacral vertebra. However, there is some obliquity. Note that the base of the spermatic cord can be seen exiting the superficial ring of the inguinal canal on the right side, but not on the left. The walls of the bladder can be discerned, but neither the prostate nor the urethra are present. Note the closely appressed rectum and seminal vesicles.

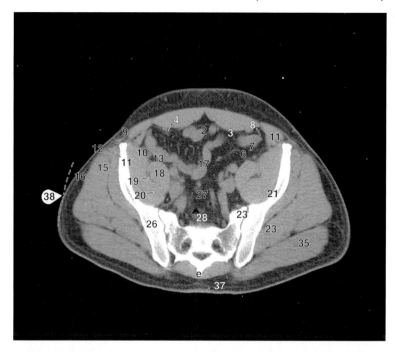

Cryosection. This section passes through the center of the fifth sacral vertebra. All three portions of the innominate bone (os coxae of the pelvis) meet in the acetabulum and are visible in this section. The spermatic cord passed through the superficial ring superior to this section. The femoral artery, vein, and nerve pass under the inguinal ligament superior to this plane. The paired seminal vesicles are lateral to the paired vas ampullae (termination of ductus deferens). The iliacus and psoas muscles merged into a single muscle, the iliopsoas within the pelvis. This muscle has now slipped over the pelvic brim on its way to the lesser trochanter. The now lateral position of the gluteus medius and minimus muscles, near tensor fascia lata, suggest their role in hip stabilization (abduction) when the contralateral foot is off the ground. Note that the iliotibial tract now spans the tensor fascia lata muscle and gluteus maximus muscle, providing hip abductor (lateral) muscle stabilization. The superior rectal vessels are now clearly visualized as they pass through pararectal fat. Just inferior to the floor of the levator ani muscle, the ischiorectal fossa is seen.

Diagnostic Image. Axial CT section that passes through the base of the fifth sacral vertebra. This patient has prostate cancer. This CT image is taken after implantation of radioactive seeds the size of rice grains. Injection of these seeds (brachytherapy) is guided by matching a transrectal ultrasound image to a preoperative CT image (the patient is asleep.) The radioactive seeds are the bright white foci within the prostate. Note their asymmetric placement to the left where a carcinoma is located (not seen). A Foley catheter with its balloon is seen in the base of the bladder.

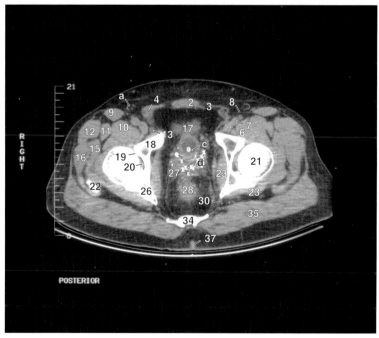

PLATE 4-4 OBTURATOR CANAL *(Visible Man 1895)*

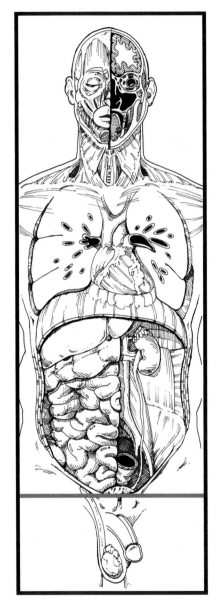

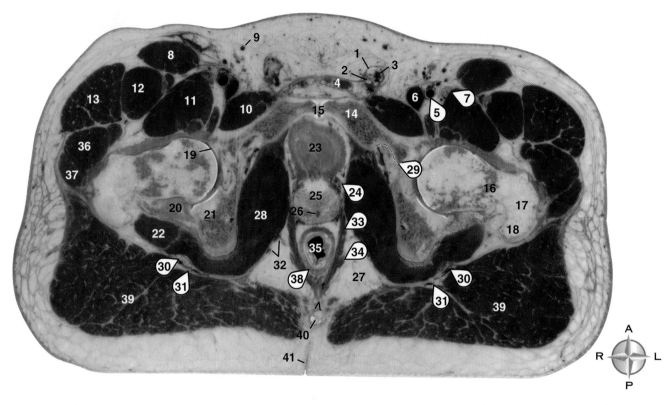

1 Spermatic cord	18 Intertrochanteric crest	33 Ilicoccygeus portion of the
2 Vas deferens	19 Acetabulum	levator ani muscle
3 Pampiniform plexus of veins	20 Labrum	34 Pubococcygeus muscle
4 Rectus abdominis muscle	21 Ischium	35 Rectum
5 Femoral artery	22 Quadratus femoris muscle	36 Gluteus medius muscle
6 Femoral vein	23 Urinary bladder	37 Gluteus minimus muscle
7 Femoral nerve	24 Seminal vesicles	38 External anal sphincter
8 Sartorius muscle	25 Prostate	39 Gluteus maximus muscle
9 Great saphenous vein	26 Prostatic urethra	40 Coccyx
10 Pectineus muscle	27 Ischiorectal fossa	41 Cluneal groove
11 Iliopsoas muscle	28 Obturator internus muscle	
12 Rectus femoris muscle	29 Obturator groove of the	## RADIOGRAPHIC KEY
13 Tensor fascia lata muscle	obturator foramina	
14 Superior pubic ramus	30 Sciatic nerve	a Linea alba
15 Pubic symphysis	31 Inferior gluteal artery and nerve	b Obturator vessels
16 Femoral neck	32 Pudendal canal with pudendal	c Quadrate tubercle
17 Greater trochanter	artery, vein, and nerve	d Ilitibial tract
of the femur		

PLATE 4-4 OBTURATOR CANAL *(Visible Man 1895)*

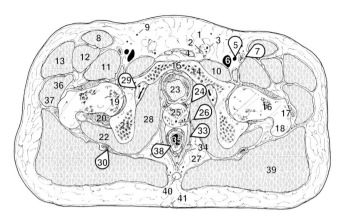

Cryosection. This section passes through the inferior portion of the superior pubic ramus and the inferior portion of the coccyx. Note the obturator vessels and nerve passing through the obturator canal at the superolateral portion of the obturator foramen. A dotted line (right side) highlights the discontinuity between the inferiormost obturator internus muscle and the superiormost quadratus femoris muscle. This plane passes through the intertrochanteric crest and greater trochanters of the femur. The femoral neck is found medial to the greater trochanter.

Corresponding CT. Homologous section to the cryosection view. It passes through the inferior portion of the acetabulum and the superior pubic ramus. The obturator vessels are seen to occupy the bony obturator canal that is found at the superior edge of the obturator foramen of the pelvis.

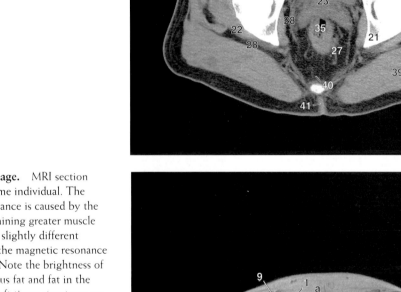

Diagnostic Image. MRI section through the same individual. The rounder appearance is caused by the patient's maintaining greater muscle tonus and by a slightly different positioning in the magnetic resonance (MR) scanner. Note the brightness of the subcutaneous fat and fat in the pelvis. Pelvic soft tissue structures are well delineated by the differences in MRI signal from fat, muscle, and bone. Note the bright fat signal within the bone marrow, a tissue that contains a large amount of fat. Note the obturator canal.

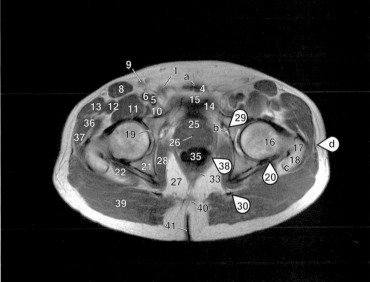

PLATE 4-5 SUPERIOR PELVIC OUTLET *(Visible Man 1903)*

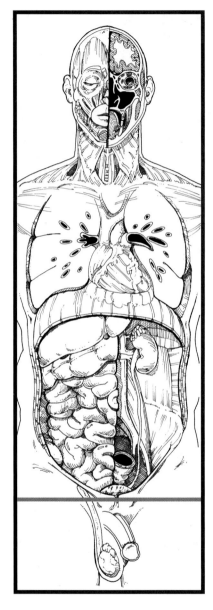

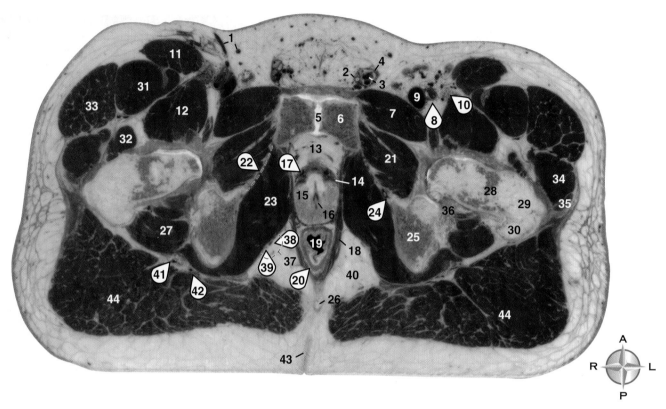

1	Great saphenous vein	17	Seminal vesicle	
2	Vas deferens	18	Puborectalis muscle	
3	Pampiniform plexus of veins	19	Rectum	
4	Spermatic cord	20	External anal sphincter muscle	
5	Pubic symphysis	21	Obturator externus muscle	
6	Pubis	22	Obturator externus membrane	
7	Pectineus muscle	23	Obturator internus muscle	
8	Femoral artery	24	Obturator vessels and nerve	
9	Femoral vein	25	Ischium	
10	Femoral nerve	26	Coccyx	
11	Sartorius muscle	27	Quadratus femoris muscle	
12	Iliopsoas muscle	28	Femoral neck	
13	Urinary bladder	29	Greater trochanter of the femur	
14	Prostatic venous plexus	30	Quadrate tubercle	
15	Prostate	31	Rectus femoris muscle	
16	Urethral crest within the prostatic urethra	32	Vastus lateralis muscle	

33	Tensor fascia lata muscle
34	Gluteus medius muscle
35	Gluteus minimis muscle
36	Labrum
37	Pudendal canal
38	Internal pudendal vessels
39	Pudendal nerve
40	Ischiorectal fossa
41	Sciatic nerve
42	Inferior gluteal vessels
43	Cluneal groove
44	Gluteus maximus muscle

RADIOGRAPHIC KEY

a Iliotibial tract

PLATE 4-5 SUPERIOR PELVIC OUTLET *(Visible Man 1903)*

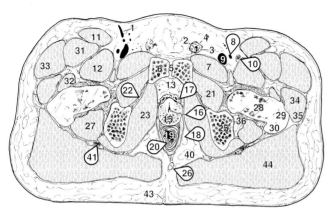

Corresponding CT. Section that passes through the same level as the cryosection, just inferior to the acetabulum and femoral head. The greater trochanter and femoral neck narrow in their approach toward the femoral diaphysis. Both spermatic cords have now emerged from the inguinal canal to enter into the scrotum. The prostate gland is situated below the bladder. Neither its associated structures nor the urethra can be differentiated on this non-contrast CT image.

Cryosection. This section passes through the pubic symphysis. The right great saphenous vein can be seen to drain, through the saphenous opening of the fascia lata, into the femoral vein. The prominence of the urethral crest suggests that the ejaculatory ducts enter the prostatic sinus on either side at or near this level. This plane is approximately midway through the obturator foramen. Note that the obturator vessels and nerve have entered the adductor muscle compartment. Below the superior pubic ramus, the pectineus muscle of the adductor compartment of the lower limb is in view. Note the approximation of the obturator internus and the obturator externus muscles on the dashed line representing the obturator membrane. The bursa between the obturator internus and the gluteus maximus muscles prevents adhesion as the latter muscle rides up and down during hip flexion and extension.

Diagnostic Image. Same section as the cryosection and the CT. MR shows internal structure of the prostate more clearly than CT. Observe increased tonus (superior rounding) on the posterior surface of both the CT and the MR images. MR allows differentiation of the prostate from the urinary bladder anterior to it. The prostate gland can be clearly differentiated from the rectum. The urethra is not clearly visualized on this image, but it is often visible with MR.

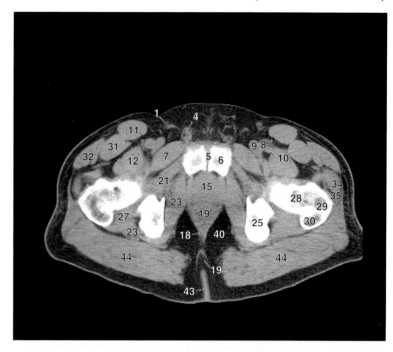

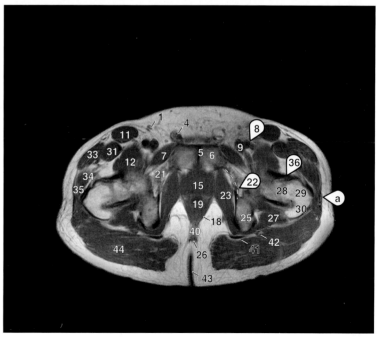

PLATE 4-6 DEEP PERINEAL POUCH AND LESSER TROCHANTER *(Visible Man 1921)*

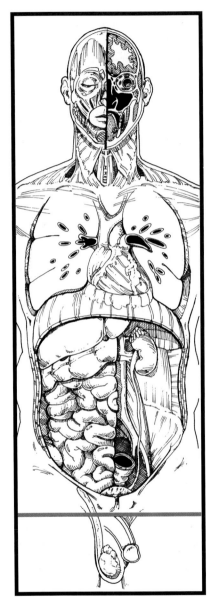

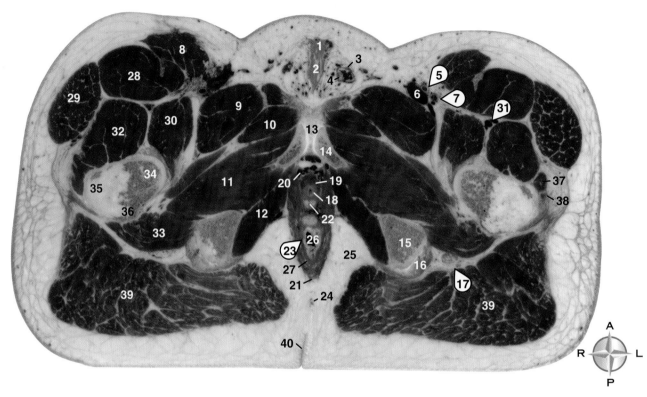

1 Corpora cavernosa	**16** Bursa of the ischial tuberosity
2 Suspensory ligament	and common origin of the
of the penis	hamstring muscles
3 Spermatic cord	**17** Sciatic nerve
4 Vas deferens	**18** Membranous urethra
5 Femoral artery	**19** Sphincter urethra muscle
6 Femoral vein	**20** Prostatic venous plexus
7 Femoral nerve	**21** Pubococcygeus muscle
8 Sartorius muscle	**22** Perineal body
9 Pectineus muscle	**23** External anal sphincter muscle
10 Adductor brevis muscle	**24** Coccyx
11 Obturator externus muscle	**25** Ischiorectal fossa
12 Obturator internus muscle	**26** Rectum
13 Pubic symphysis	**27** Puborectalis muscle
14 Inferior pubic ramus	**28** Rectus femoris muscle
15 Ischial tuberosity	

29 Tensor fascia lata muscle
30 Iliopsoas muscle
31 Lateral circumflex vein
32 Vastus lateralis muscle
33 Quadratus femoris muscle
34 Femoral neck
35 Greater trochanter of the femur
36 Pectineal line of the femur
37 Gluteus medius muscle
38 Gluteus minimis muscle
39 Gluteus maximus muscle
40 Cluneal groove

RADIOGRAPHIC KEY

a Iliotibial tract

PLATE 4-6 DEEP PERINEAL POUCH AND LESSER TROCHANTER *(Visible Man 1921)*

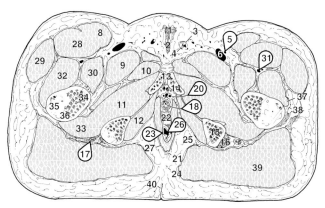

Corresponding CT. Section that passes through the same level as the cryosection. Now inferior to the inferior pubic and ischial rami, the hip adductor, abductor, and quadriceps compartments are distinctive. The deep perineal pouch structures, including the urethra, and rectum cannot be differentiated.

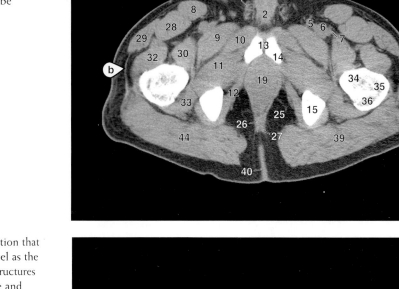

Cryosection. This section passes through the deep perineal space. The membranous urethra, sphincter urethra muscle, and deep transversus perinei muscle, all deep perineal space structures, are visible. This section also passes through the base of the pubic symphysis and the inferior ischial rami. The spermatic cord on the right side is drastically reduced as the Visible Man had an undescended testicle on this side. The iliopsoas muscle can be seen to insert on the lesser trochanter. The vastus lateralis muscle is well visualized in this section, whereas the previously larger tensor fascia latae is becoming substantially encased in the fascia from which its name derives. The obturator externus muscle is inserting into the trochanteric fossa just medial to the quadratus femoris insertion. Anteromedial to these two insertions, note the formation of the iliopsoas tendon as it passes inferiorly.

Corresponding MR. Section that passes through the same level as the cryosection. The internal structures and relations of the prostate and rectum are well visualized. This image shows the tendinous origin of the hamstring muscles on the posterolateral surface of the ischial tuberosity. The deep perineal pouch structures, including the urethra, and rectum can be differentiated.

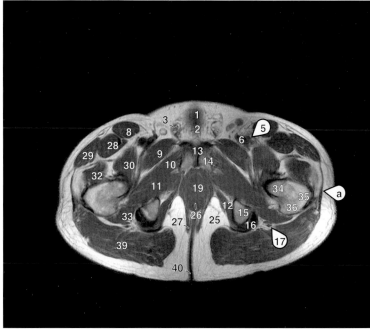

PLATE 4-7 BULB OF THE PENIS *(Visible Man 1940)*

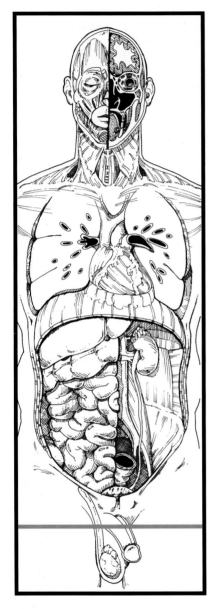

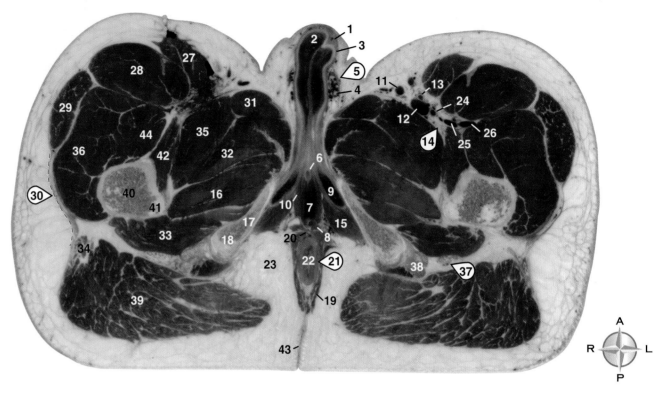

1	Dorsal vein of the penis	15	Obturator internus muscle	30	Iliotibial tract
2	Corpus cavernosum	16	Obturator externus muscle	31	Adductor longus muscle
3	Tunica albuginea of the penis	17	Inferior ischial ramus	32	Adductor brevis muscle
4	Vas deferens	18	Ischial tuberosity	33	Quadratus femoris muscle
5	Spermatic cord	19	Puborectalis muscle	34	Gluteus maximus muscle tendon
6	Spongy urethra	20	Perineal body	35	Pectineus muscle
7	Bulb of the penis	21	External anal sphincter	36	Vastus lateralis muscle
8	Muscular coating of the bulb of the penis	22	Rectum	37	Sciatic nerve
		23	Pararectal fat	38	Biceps femoris tendon
9	Crus of the penis	24	Profunda femoris artery	39	Gluteus maximus muscle
10	Ischiocavernosus muscle of the right crus of the penis	25	Profunda femoris vein	40	Femoral shaft (diaphysis)
		26	Lateral circumflex vein	41	Pectineal line of the femur
11	Great saphenous vein	27	Sartorius muscle	42	Iliopsoas muscle
12	Femoral vein	28	Rectus femoris muscle	43	Cluneal groove
13	Femoral artery	29	Tensor fascia lata muscle	44	Vastus intermedius muscle
14	Femoral nerve				

PLATE 4-7 BULB OF THE PENIS *(Visible Man 1940)*

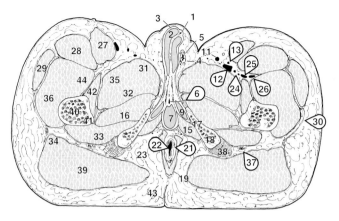

Corresponding CT. Section that passes through the same level as the cryosection. An in vivo view of the femoral vessels and nerve in the adductor canal presents better definition to the patent vessels and nerve. This level is somewhat more cranial to the corresponding MR image as the puborectalis muscle can be seen. The crura and bulb of the penis cannot be differentiated from each other or the rectum in this non-contrast CT scan.

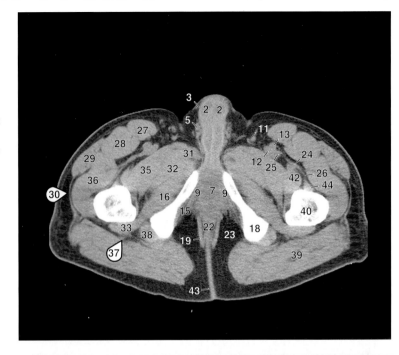

Cryosection. Section that passes through the inferiormost ischial tuberosity and inferior ischial ramus, the inferiormost structures of the pelvis. This slice highlights the structures of the bulb of the penis. The crura present the ischiocavernosus muscle covering of the erectile tissue within the right and the left crura. The equivalent layers of the bulb of the penis, corpus cavernosus and corpus spongiosum are seen centrally to surround the spongy urethra. The inferior limits of the puborectalis surround the rectum. The adductor longus and sartorius muscles delimit the lateral borders of the adductor canal. The inferior insertion of the quadratus femoris and the iliopsoas muscles come directly to the lesser trochanter. This section appears to be at the inferiormost part of the lesser trochanter, evidenced by the iliopsoas fibers that appear to override it near its medial extent. With the thickened fascia lata joining the tensor fascia lata and the gluteus maximus muscles, the iliotibial tract now prevents the vastus lateralis muscle from bowstringing.

Corresponding MR. Section that passes through the same level as the cryosection. MR commonly provides better resolution to complex soft-tissue structures than CT, and this is seen here in the penile anatomy. Note that the crura can be differentiated from the bulb in MR. This level is somewhat caudal to the corresponding CT image as it appears that the rectum is transitioning to anus. As in Plate 4-7, the common hamstring origin on the inferolateral portion of the ischial tuberosity is well visualized.

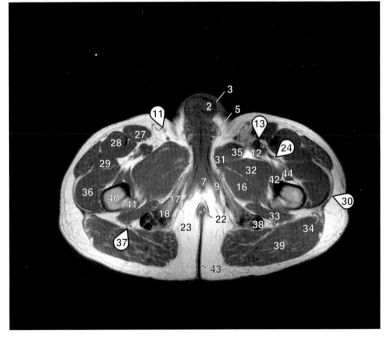

PLATE 4-8 EXTERNAL PENIS *(Visible Man 1958)*

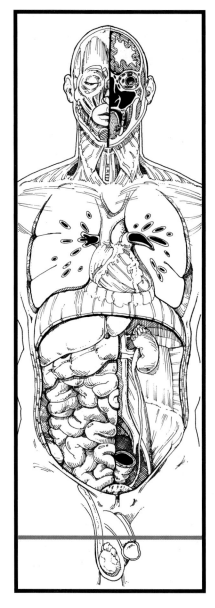

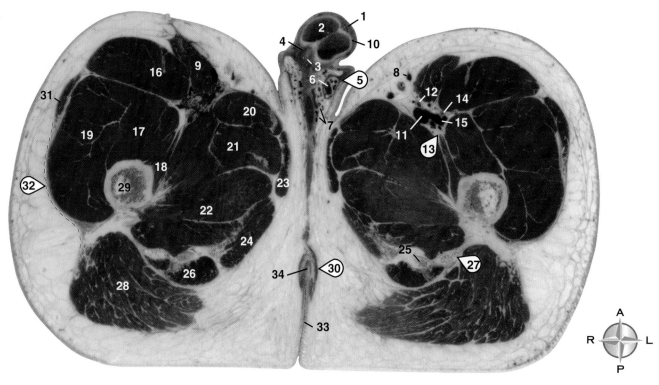

1	Dorsal vein of the penis	**14**	Profunda femoris artery	**24**	Semimembranous muscle
2	Corpus cavernosum	**15**	Profunda femoris vein	**25**	Semitendinosus tendon
3	Spongy urethra	**16**	Rectus femoris muscle	**26**	Biceps femoris muscle and tendon
4	Corpus spongiosum	**17**	Vastus intermedius muscle	**27**	Sciatic nerve
5	Spermatic cord	**18**	Vastus medialis muscle	**28**	Gluteus maximus muscle
6	Vas deferens	**19**	Vastus lateralis muscle	**29**	Femoral shaft (diaphysis)
7	Pampiniform plexus	**20**	Adductor longus muscle	**30**	External anal sphincter muscle
8	Great saphenous vein	**21**	Adductor brevis muscle	**31**	Tensor fascia lata muscle
9	Sartorius muscle	**22**	Adductor magnus muscle	**32**	Iliotibial tract
10	Tunica albuginea of the penis	**23**	Gracilis muscle	**33**	Cluneal groove
11	Femoral vein			**34**	Anus
12	Femoral artery				
13	Femoral nerve				

PLATE 4-8 EXTERNAL PENIS *(Visible Man 1958)*

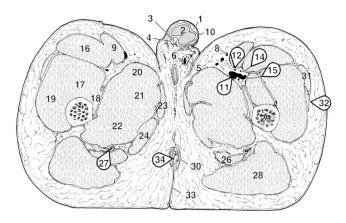

Cryosection. This section passes through the shaft of the femur just inferior to the lesser trochanter. The missing spermatic cord on right evidences an undescended testicle. The pendulous portion of the penis presents the two corpus cavernosa dorsal (anterior) to the corpus spongiosum. The gracilis muscle is now seen as is the characteristic arrangement of the semimembranosus muscle and the tendon of the semitendinosus muscle. The biceps femoris muscle is seen covering the medial portion of the sciatic nerve. Inferiorly it envelops this nerve.

Corresponding CT. Section that passes through the same level as the cryosection. The hamstring muscles are now distinguishable on the right side. However, muscles in the other compartments are more difficult to separate visually. The dense tunica albuginea is seen as a white line surrounding the penile compartments. Unlike the Visible Man, both vas deferens can be visualized.

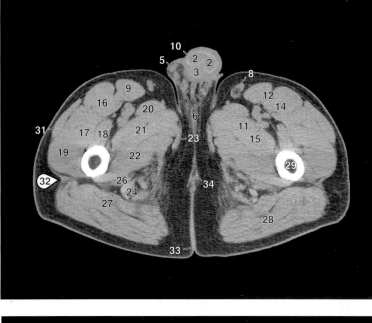

Corresponding MR. Section that passes through the same level as the cryosection. The muscular thigh and penile anatomy can be made out with much greater resolution than in the matching CT image. The dense, nearly avascular, tunica albuginea (visceral layer of the tunica vaginalis) is seen as a darker line around the cavernosal tissue of the penis.

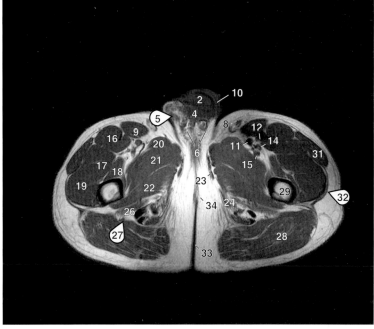

PLATE 4-9 **TESTICLE** *(Visible Man 1990)*

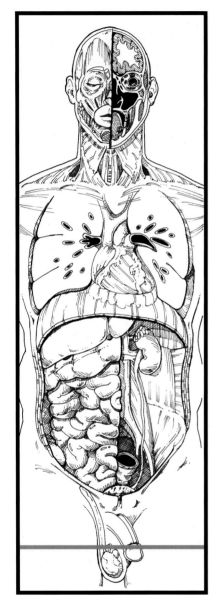

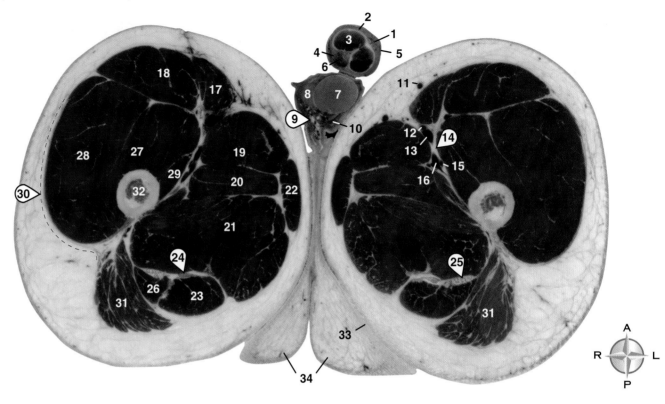

1   Dorsal vein of the penis
2   Tunica albuginea of the penis
3   Corpus cavernosum
4   Corpus spongiousum
5   Corona of the glans penis
6   Spongy urethra
7   Testis
8   Epididymis
9   Vas deferens
10 Pampiniform plexus
11 Great saphenous vein
12 Femoral artery
13 Femoral vein
14 Femoral nerve

15 Profunda femoris artery
16 Profunda femoris vein
17 Sartorius muscle
18 Rectus femoris muscle
19 Adductor longus muscle
20 Adductor brevis muscle
21 Adductor magnus muscle
22 Gracilis muscle
23 Semimembranosus muscle
24 Semitendinosus tendon
25 Sciatic nerve
26 Biceps femoris muscle

27 Vastus intermedius muscle
28 Vastus lateralis muscle
29 Vastus medialis muscle
30 Iliotibial tract
31 Gluteus maximus muscle
32 Femoral shaft (diaphysis)
33 Gluteal fold
34 Buttocks

RADIOGRAPHIC KEY

a   Tensor fascia lata muscle
b   Cluneal groove
c   Tunica albuginea

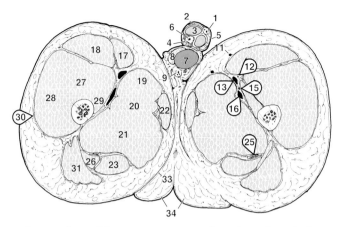

PLATE 4-9 TESTICLE *(Visible Man 1990)*

Corresponding CT. Homologous level as in the Visible Man cryosection image. However, the testicles are inferior to this level. However, still present, the tensor fascia lata muscle extends more inferiorly in this individual than in the Visible Man. The distinctive anatomy of the semitendinosus muscle seated within the semimembranosus muscle is better distinguished in this image than in the cryosection.

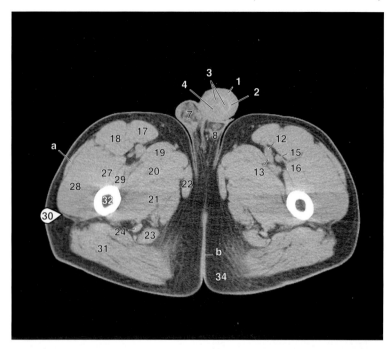

Cryosection. This section passes nearly midway through the upper third of the femur as well as through the glans penis. The right testicle is missing, as it never descended. The superiormost left epididymis is seen. The three thigh muscle compartments (i.e., quadriceps, adductor, and hamstring) are visible. The gluteal fold is seen between the buttocks and the posteromedial thigh.

Diagnostic Image. Sagittal ultrasound of testis. The head of the epididymis is seen as a pyramidal structure at the top of the testis. Note homogeneous texture of this normal testis. (Key: A, anterior; I, inferior; P, posterior; S, superior.)

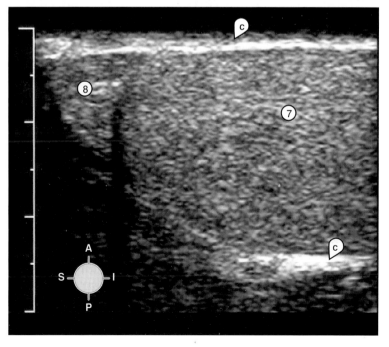

PLATE 4-10 FEMALE PELVIS: ACETABULUM *(Visible Woman 1825)*

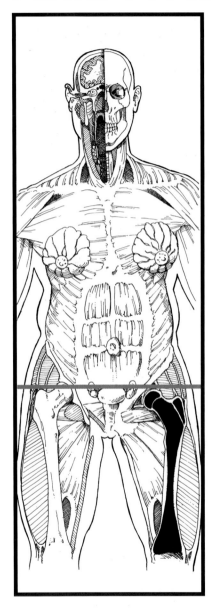

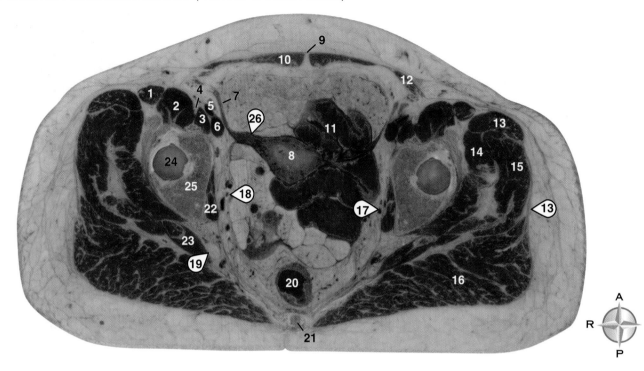

1 Sartorius muscle
2 Iliacus muscle
3 Psoas muscle
4 Femoral nerve
5 External iliac artery
6 External iliac vein
7 Round ligament
8 Fundus of the uterus
9 Linea alba
10 Rectus abdominis muscle
11 Ileum portion of the small intestine
12 Transversus abdominis muscle
13 Tensor fascia lata muscle and tendon
14 Gluteus minimis muscle
15 Gluteus medius muscle
16 Gluteus maximus muscle
17 Left ureter

18 Right ureter
19 Sciatic nerve
20 Rectum
21 Fifth sacral vertebra
22 Obturator internus muscle
23 Piriformis muscle
24 Head of the femur
25 Ilium portion of the pelvis
26 Broad ligament

RADIOGRAPHIC KEY

a Right ovary
b Left ovary
c Bladder
d Fluid in cul-de-sac

PLATE 4-1O FEMALE PELVIS: ACETABULUM *(Visible Woman 1825)*

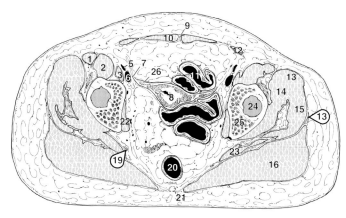

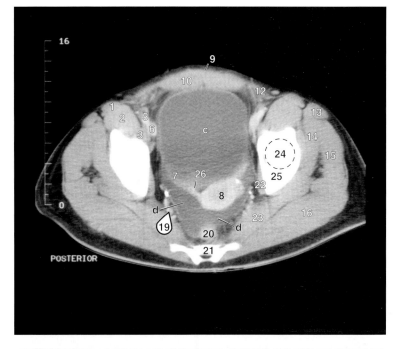

Corresponding CT. Section passes through the lower fourth sacral vertebra. The uterus is shifted to the left in this individual. Outside of pregnancy, the position of the uterus shifts in response to bladder and rectal contents. The external iliac vessels are enhanced by contrast medium. The bright spots lateral to the ischiorectal fossae are vessels in the pudendal canal. Note fluid within the cul-de-sac, which is well delineated by the fluid.

Cryosection. This section passes through the fifth sacral vertebra, as well as the superiormost region of the femoral head as it sits under the ilial portion of the acetabulum. This level is within the true pelvis (between the pelvic inlet and outlet). An area where many obstetric dimensions are taken. Although much of the other anatomy is mediolaterally wide compared with male anatomy, the pelvic cavity appears anteroposteriorly broad at this level. Despite neither fallopian tube nor ovary being visible, the mesentery covering this portion of the uterus, the broad ligament, can be seen to extend laterally as the round ligament. The inguinal ligament is below the round ligament's entrance into the inguinal canal. The external iliac vessels and the femoral nerve pass under the inguinal ligament and into the thigh inferior to this section. This level is inferior to the ascending, descending, or sigmoid colon, as only the rectum and loops of mesentery-suspended ileum are seen.

Diagnostic Image. Axial ultrasound image somewhat superior to that in the cryosection and corresponding CT, most likely at the level of the fourth sacral vertebra. The urinary bladder is the black space anteriorly in the image. Note its thin wall. Both ovaries are seen posteriorly along their respective pelvic side walls. The uterus is not seen on this image. Bright areas are fat within the mesentary of the ovaries and pelvic ligaments. (Key: V, ventral; L, left; D, dorsal; R, right.)

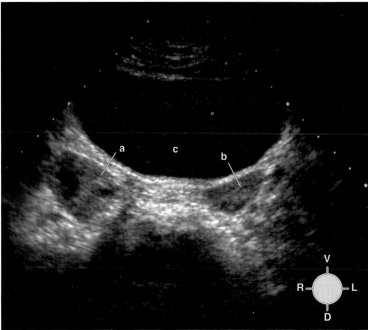

81

PLATE 4-11 FEMALE PELVIS: ACETABULUM *(Visible Woman 1845)*

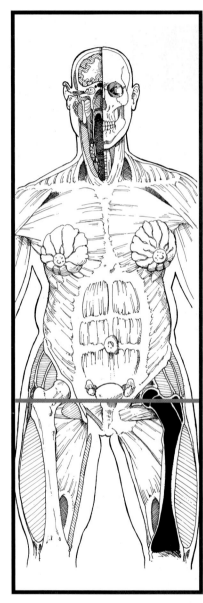

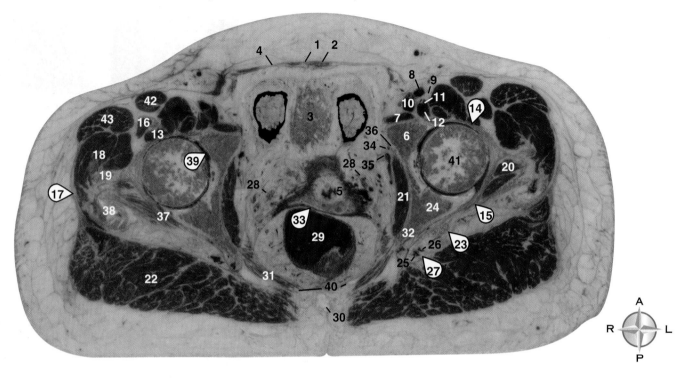

1 Linea alba	**17** Iliotibial tract	**33** Rectouterine fold
2 Rectus abdominis muscle	**18** Gluteus medius muscle	**34** Obturator artery
3 Bladder	**19** Tendon of the gluteus minimis muscle	**35** Obturator vein
4 Inguinal ligament	**20** Superior gemellus muscle	**36** Obturator nerve
5 Os of the uterine cervix	**21** Obturator internus muscle	**37** Tendon of the obturator internus muscle
6 Pubis portion of the pelvis	**22** Gluteus maximus muscle	**38** Greater trochanter of the femur
7 Pectineus muscle	**23** Sciatic nerve	**39** Acetabulum
8 Femoral artery	**24** Ischium portion of the pelvis	**40** Sacrospinous ligament
9 Femoral nerve	**25** Inferior gluteal artery	**41** Femoral head
10 Femoral vein	**26** Inferior gluteal vein	**42** Sartorius muscle
11 Psoas major muscle	**27** Inferior gluteal nerve	**43** Tensor fascia lata muscle
12 Psoas major muscle tendon	**28** Ureter	
13 Iliacus muscle	**29** Rectum	## RADIOGRAPHIC KEY
14 Anterior femoral labrum (iliofemoral ligament)	**30** Coccyx	**a** Myometrium
15 Posterior femoral labrum (ischiofemoral ligament)	**31** Coccygeus muscle	**b** Endometrium
16 Rectus femoris muscle	**32** Ischial spine	**c** Fluid in cul-de-sac

PLATE 4-11 FEMALE PELVIS: ACETABULUM (Visible Woman 1845)

Corresponding CT. Section that passes through the fifth sacral vertebra. This section presents the body of the uterus. The more dense (external) myometrial layer is discernible from the internal (endometrial) layer. The outline of the femoral head is discernible. Plates 4-10 and 4-11 depict the external iliac artery and vein passing under the inguinal ligament to become the femoral artery and vein. The latter vessels are seen within the femoral sheath of the adductor canal in the thigh. These vessels, as well as the pudendal vessels, are enhanced by contrast agent.

Cryosection. This section passes through the coccyx. It presents the internal cervical os of the uterus. It also shows how the ureters course anteriorly in the base of the pelvis, inferior to the mesentery. Note how the mediolaterally wide femoral head (and femur in general) result in a somewhat broader femoral labrum. This puts strain on ligaments that would be taken up more so by bone in a male. As opposed to Plate 4-10 and male anatomy, the shape of the pelvis, here the pelvic outlet, can also be seen to be mediolaterally wide. The subcutaneous thick fatty layer posterolaterally is also more characteristic of females than males.

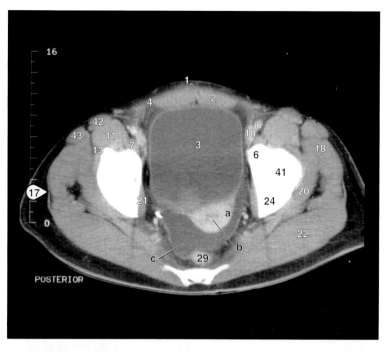

Diagnostic Image. Axial ultrasound image somewhat superior to that in the cryosection and corresponding CT, most likely at the level of the fifth sacral vertebra. The dark area anteriorly is the urinary bladder as in Plate 4–10. The transverse view of the uterus shows the outer myometrium and brighter inner endometrium. (Key: V, ventral; L, left; D, dorsal; R, right.)

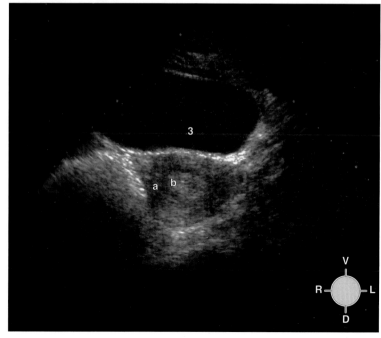

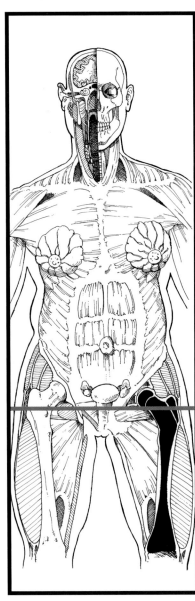

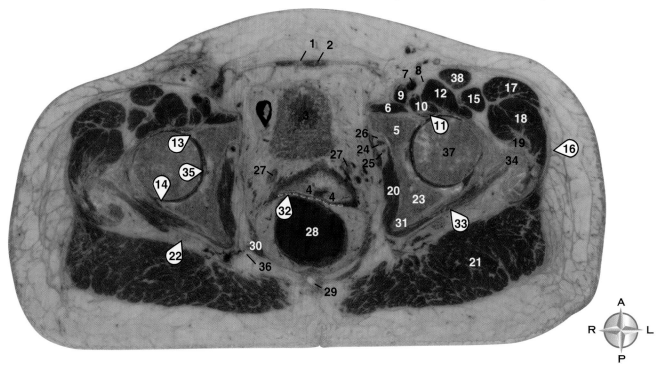

1 Linea alba	**19** Tendon of the gluteus minimis muscle	**38** Sartorius muscle
2 Rectus abdominis muscle	**20** Obturator internus muscle	
3 Bladder	**21** Gluteus maximus muscle	## RADIOGRAPHIC KEY
4 Lateral fornices of the os of the uterine cervix	**22** Sciatic nerve	**a** Fifth lumbar vertebra
5 Pubis portion of the pelvis	**23** Ischium portion of the pelvis	**b** Sacrum
6 Pectineus muscle	**24** Obturator artery	**c** Sacroiliac joint
7 Femoral artery	**25** Obturator vein	**d** Ischial tuberosity
8 Femoral nerve	**26** Obturator nerve	**e** Superior ischial ramus
9 Femoral vein	**27** Ureter	**f** Inferior ischial ramus
10 Psoas major muscle	**28** Rectum	**g** Superior pubic ramus
11 Psoas major muscle tendon	**29** Coccyx	**h** Inferior pubic ramus
12 Iliacus muscle	**30** Coccygeus muscle	**i** Pubic symphysis
13 Anterior femoral labrum (iliofemoral ligament)	**31** Ischial spine	**j** Iliac crest
14 Posterior femoral labrum (ischiofemoral ligament)	**32** Rectouterine fold	**k** Anterior superior iliac spine
	33 Tendon of the obturator internus muscle	**l** Anterior inferior iliac spine
15 Rectus femoris muscle	**34** Greater trochanter of the femur	**m** Greater trochanter of the femur
16 Iliotibial tract	**35** Acetabulum	**n** Lesser trochanter of the femur
17 Tensor fascia lata muscle	**36** Sacrospinous ligament	**o** Uterine cervix
18 Gluteus medius muscle	**37** Femoral head	**p** Fifth sacral vertebra
		q Pudendal vessels
		r Fluid in cul-de-sac

PLATE 4-12 FEMALE PELVIS: FORNICES OF UTERINE CERVICAL OS *(Visible Woman 1850)*

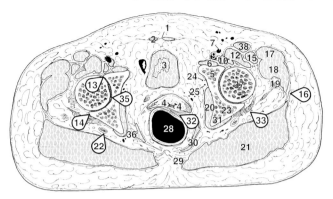

Cryosection. This section passes through the coccyx. This level presents the fornices that surround the external uterine os cervix as it transitions caudally into the vagina. The cervical canal can be of varying lengths. The obliquity of this cut through the pubic superior rami gives the appearance that they course, in subsequent inferior slices, through the more medial bladder. However, the superior pubic rami are thick and are oriented more anteromedially as can be seen in Plate 4-13.

Corresponding CT. Section that passes through the fifth sacral vertebra. It presents the cervical region of the uterus. A distended bladder dominates the pelvis at this level. This section is roughly halfway through the femoral head and acetabulum. The femoral artery and vein, as well as the pudendal vessels, are enhanced by contrast agent.

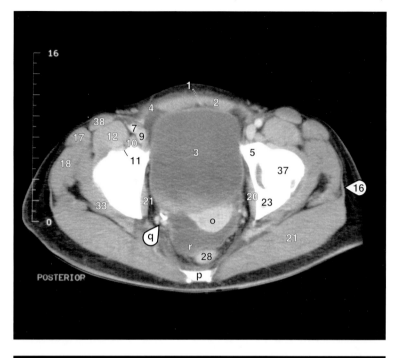

Diagnostic Image. Posterior-to-anterior plain-film pyelogram radiograph. Contrast in the urine highlights the ureters and bladder in this female patient. Note the gynecoid shape of the pelvic inlet, largely caused by the great breadth of the pubic rami and sacrum.

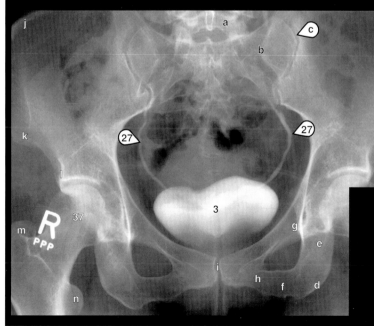

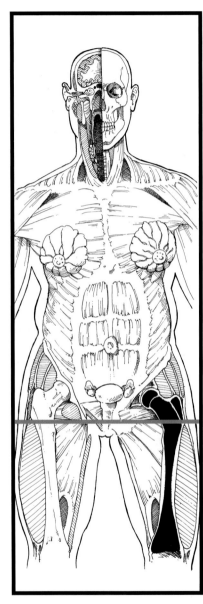

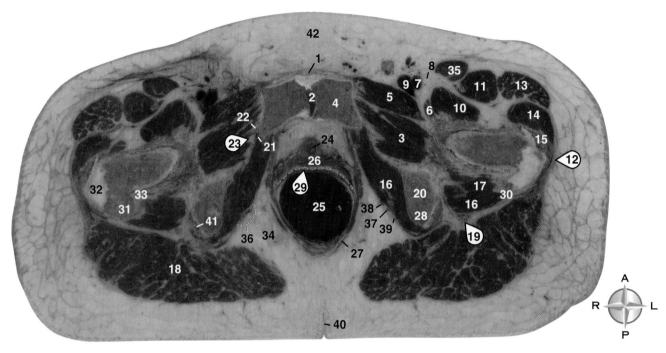

1 Linea alba	18 Gluteus maximus muscle	35 Sartorius muscle
2 Pubic symphysis	19 Sciatic nerve	36 Pudendal canal
3 Obturator externus muscle	20 Ischium portion of the pelvis	37 Pudendal artery
4 Pubis portion of the pelvis	21 Obturator artery	38 Pudendal vein
5 Adductor brevis muscle	22 Obturator vein	39 Pudendal nerve
6 Pectineus muscle	23 Obturator nerve	40 Cluneal groove
7 Femoral artery	24 Ureter	41 Origin of the biceps femoris
8 Femoral nerve	25 Rectum	muscle
9 Femoral vein	26 Vagina	42 Mons pubis
10 Iliopsoas muscle	27 Coccygeus muscle	
11 Rectus femoris muscle	28 Ischial tuberosity	**RADIOGRAPHIC KEY**
12 Iliotibial tract	29 Rectouterine fold	
13 Tensor fascia lata muscle	30 Tendon of the obturator	a Myometrium
14 Gluteus medius muscle	internus muscle	b Endometrium
15 Tendon of the gluteus minimis	31 Greater trochanter of the femur	c Uterus
muscle	32 Trochanteric bursa	d Cervix
16 Obturator internus muscle	33 Intertrochanteric fossa	e Sphincter urethra
17 Superior gemellus muscle	34 Ischiorectal fossa	f Fluid in retrouterine pouch
		(normal)

PLATE 4-13 FEMALE PELVIS: URETHRA IN DEEP PERINEAL POUCH *(Visible Woman 1870)*

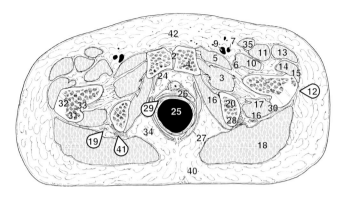

Cryosection. This section passes through the femoral neck at the level of the greater trochanter. The female (Visible Woman) urethra is seen within the deep perineal pouch that contains the sphincter urethra. Overlying the pubic symphysis anteriorly is a normally dense, fatty projection referred to as the mons pubis. Pelvic examination of pelvic structures is made easy by the distensible vagina or rectum. Note the somewhat large portion of the pelvic space now occupied by the ischiorectal fossa here and in cranial sections.

Corresponding CT. Section that passes through the femoral neck at the level of the greater trochanter. This section also passes through the deep perineal pouch. The two transverse muscular structures within the pouch are visualized by both their location (relative to the urethra, vagina, and rectum) and appearance (horizontal texture). The femoral vessels are visible, but circulating blood is not enhanced; thus the pudendal vessels cannot be discerned. The fat external to, and the trochanteric bursa internal to, the iliotibial tract allows it to be readily detected.

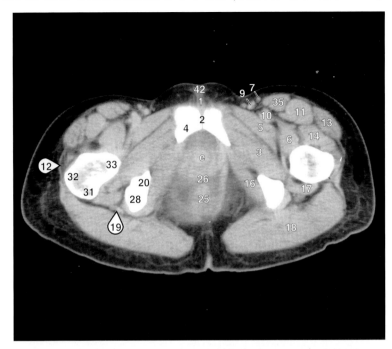

Diagnostic Image. Approximately midsagittal ultrasound image through the pubic symphysis, uterus, vagina, and rectum. The dark urinary bladder is anterior. The uterine body is clearly visualized. The myometrial and endometrial layers can be discerned. The clear area inferior to the uterus is fluid in the rectouterine pouch. The vagina is seen extending from the cervix caudally. The urethra is not included on the image. (Key: S, superior; D, dorsal; I, inferior; V, ventral.)

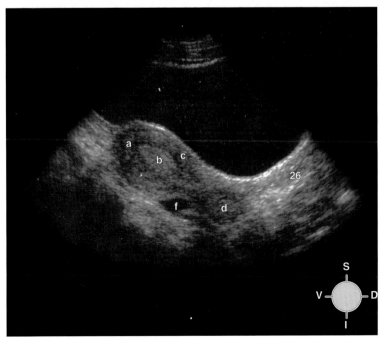

87

PLATE 4-14 FEMALE PELVIS: PELVIC OUTLET AND CLITORIS *(Visible Woman 1895)*

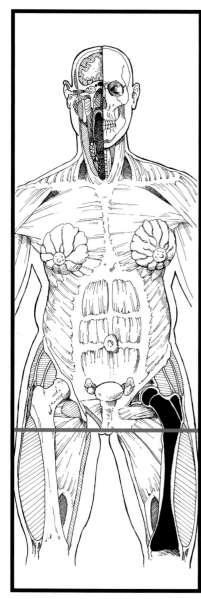

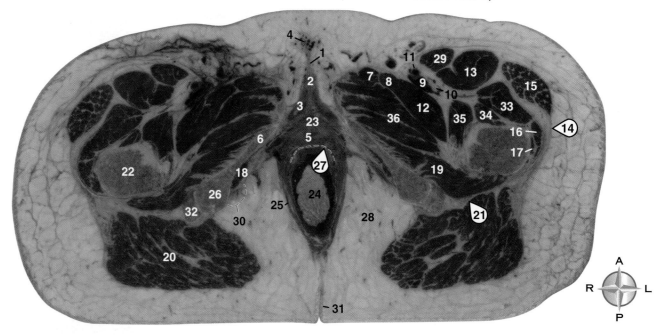

1	Suspensory ligament of the clitoris	20	Gluteus maximus muscle	b Peritoneal cavity
2	Body of the clitoris	21	Sciatic nerve	c Fundus of the uterus
3	Crus of the clitoris	22	Femoral diaphysis	d Body of the uterus
4	Clitoral vessels	23	Ureter	e Retrovesicular pouch
5	Vagina	24	Rectum	f Cervical os of the uterus
6	Inferior pubic ramus	25	Levator ani muscle	g Bladder
7	Adductor brevis muscle	26	Ischial tuberosity	h Urethra
8	Pectineus muscle	27	Rectouterine fold	i Mons pubis
9	Femoral vein	28	Ischiorectal fossa	j Pubic symphysis
10	Femoral nerve	29	Sartorius muscle	k Labia majora
11	Femoral artery	30	Pudendal canal	l Central perineal tendon
12	Adductor longus muscle	31	Cluneal groove	m Anus
13	Rectus femoris muscle	32	Origin of the biceps femoris and semitendinosus muscle	n Coccyx
14	Iliotibial tract			o Rectouterine pouch
15	Tensor fascia lata muscle	33	Vastus lateralis muscle	p Sacral promontory
16	Gluteus medius muscle	34	Vastus intermedialis muscle	q Erector spinae muscle
17	Tendon of the gluteus minimis muscle	35	Vastus medialis muscle	L Lumbar vertebrae followed by the corresponding number
18	Obturator internus muscle	36	Adductor magnus muscle	S Sacral vertebrae followed by the corresponding number
19	Obturator externus muscle			

RADIOGRAPHIC KEY

a Rectus abdominis muscle

PLATE 4-14 FEMALE PELVIS: PELVIC OUTLET AND CLITORIS *(Visible Woman 1895)*

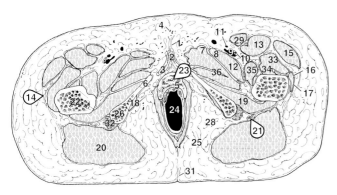

Cryosection. This section passes through the inferior ischial rami, just inferior to their junction with the inferior pubic rami. This level presents the clitoral structures that are suspended from the pubic symphysis and inferior pubic rami. The dorsal vessels just anterior to these structures provide blood to the clitoral erectile tissue.

Corresponding CT. Section that passes through the femoral diaphysis just below the greater trochanter. The inferior surface of the ischiopubic ramus is completely visible on the left side. The femoral vessels are visible, but circulating blood is not enhanced; thus the pudendal vessels cannot be discerned. The two urogenital orifices (i.e., urethra and vagina) and the anal triangle orifice (anus) are clearly discerned.

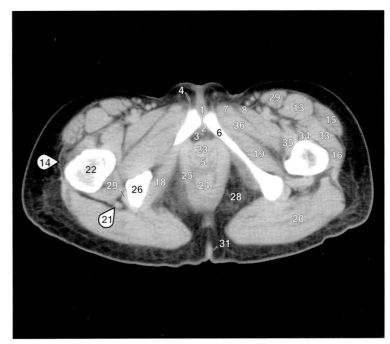

Diagnostic Image. Midsagittal pelvic MR presents the lowest peritoneal cavity through the labia majora and buttocks. The bladder is distended, thus elevating the uterus. The full bladder also reduces the potential space in the rectovesicle and rectouterine pouches. Note that in an anatomical position the pectineal (superior margin) of the pubic symphysis and the sacral promontory present a pelvic inlet that opens, primarily anteriorly. (Key: S, superior; D, dorsal; I, inferior; V, ventral.)

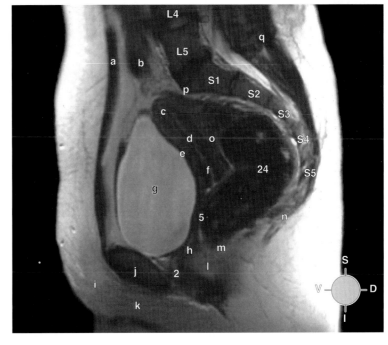

CHAPTER 5

Lower Limb

INTRODUCTION

The upper segment of the lower limb is the thigh, and the lower segment is the true, or anatomical, leg (i.e., the crura). The lower limb is both a loco-motor and a weight-bearing structure. The largest and the second largest bones in the body are the femur and the tibia, respectively. Thus, active use, high strain, and large size make these bones espe-cially susceptible to systemic processes of geriatric osteoporosis (loss of bone density). The most com-mon initial fracture site is the proximal femur, usually across the femoral neck, between the trochanters (intertrochanteric), through the troch-anters (pertrochanteric), or in the infratrochan-teric shaft (diaphysis).

The muscles of the lower limb are generally arranged in anterior (ventroflexor) and posterior (dorsiflexor) compartments. Figure 5-1 shows that the quadriceps are the primary flexors and the hamstrings the primary extensors of the thigh and the hip. There is an additional medial compart-ment of hip adductors that counterpose the hip abductors (gluteus medius, gluteus minimus, and tensor fascia lata). There is no adductor compart-ment in the calf (i.e., the anatomical leg). How-ever, there is a lateral compartment that laterally flexes the foot at the ankle (peroneus brevis and peroneus longus).

The lower limb is medially rotated about the knee, as evidenced by the medial location of the first digit (cf., lateral location in the upper limb) in anatomical position. This is also why the dorsal sur-face of the foot is found ventrally. Embryologically,

FIGURE 5-1 Serial Relation of Flexor and Extensor Compartments.   As with the upper limb, the general arrangement finds flexors anteriorly and extensors posteriorly. However, the matter is complicated by (a) medial rotation of the foot about the knee, (b) an adductor compartment in the medial thigh, and (c) a lateral flexor compartment in the medial calf. Key: Plate 5-2: (1) hip flexor, knee extensor, and thigh abductor muscles, (2) hip adductor muscles, (3) hip extensor (hamstring) muscles; Plate 5-3: (4) knee extensor muscles, (5) hip adductor muscles, (6) Plate 5-7: (7) superficial foot dorsiflexor muscles, (8) deep foot plantar flexor muscles, (9) lateral foot dorsiflexor muscles, (10) foot plantar-flexor muscles; Plate 5-8: (11) foot dorsiflexor muscles, (12) lateral foot dorsiflexor muscles, (13) foot plantar-flexor muscles; Plate 5-12 (14) digital dorsiflexor muscles, (15) digital plantar-flexor muscles.

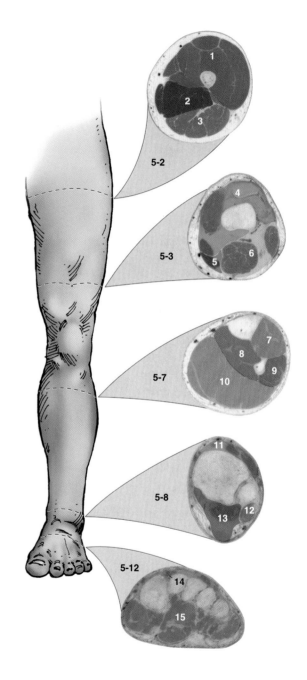

before medial rotation of the foot, the dorsal surface of the foot is also posterior to the plantar surface.

The three joints of the lower limb (i.e., hip, knee, ankle) have restricted and serially different flexion angles. The hip is a primarily ventriflexing joint; the knee is a primarily dorsiflexing joint; and the foot flexes in both directions, which is a requirement for normal walking. However, the muscular and bony anatomy and geometry of the ankle result in more powerful plantarflexion at the ankle than dorsiflexion. The movements at joints in the lower limb, in general, are more restricted owing to large ligamentous structures, such as the labrum about the femoral head. Muscular tendon insertions also tend to limit displacement move-ments at the joints, such that portions of bones or articular capsules may break off along with torn tendons in catastrophic fracture situations.

All plates after 5-1 present only the left leg. The plates depict the following:
5-1, a section that passes midway through the femoral head in the acetabulum
5-2, a section that passes through the middle of the femoral diaphysis

5-3, a section just superior to the knee joint

5-4, a section that passes precisely through the knee joint

5-5, a section that passes just inferior to the knee joint

5-6, a section that divides the superior 1/5 and inferior 4/5 of the calf

5-7, a section that is between the superior 2/3 and the lower 1/3 of the calf

5-8, a section just superior to the ankle joint at the level of the superior extensor retinaculum

5-9, a section that passes through the upper ankle (talocrural) joint

5-10, a section that transects the lower ankle (subtalar) joint

Notes are made where the cryosection images of the Visible Man are inconsistent with what would be seen were he in anatomical position.

From the knee distally, his legs are medially rotated and his feet are plantar flexed. For the anatomy of the feet to be shown better, the last two Visible Man cryosection images were replanarized to represent views seen in anatomical position. Plate 5-11 presents a cut through the midtarsal region. The most distal view, Plate 5-12, shows a section that passes through the mid-metatarsal region.

PLATE 5-1 LEFT THIGH: FEMORAL HEAD *(Visible Man 1880)*

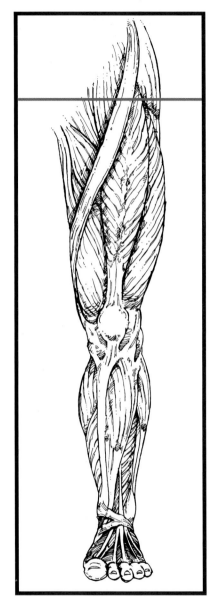

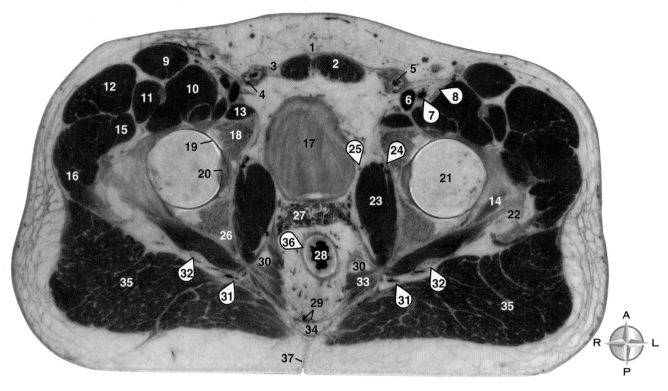

1	Linea alba	15	Gluteus minimis muscle	29	Superior rectal vessels
2	Rectus abdominis muscle	16	Gluteus medius muscle	30	Ischiorectal fossa
3	Linea semilunares	17	Urinary bladder	31	Inferior gluteal vessels
4	Spermatic cord	18	Pubis	32	Sciatic nerve
5	Vas deferens	19	Acetabulum	33	Levator ani muscle
6	Femoral vein	20	Ligamentum teres muscle	34	Fifth sacral vertebra
7	Femoral artery	21	Head of the femur	35	Gluteus maximus muscle
8	Femoral nerve	22	Greater trochanter of the femur	36	External muscular coat of the rectum
9	Sartorius muscle	23	Obturator internus muscle		
10	Iliopsoas muscle	24	Obturator vessels	37	Cluneal groove
11	Rectus femoris muscle	25	Obturator nerve		
12	Tensor fascia lata muscle	26	Ischial spine		**RADIOGRAPHIC KEY**
13	Pectineus muscle	27	Seminal vesicles	a	Lymph node
14	Ilium	28	Rectum		

PLATE 5-1 LEFT THIGH: FEMORAL HEAD (Visible Man 1880)

Corresponding Computed Tomography (CT). Note that the muscle tonus of this live patient elevates the lateral borders of the hips and rounds the cluneal region. Similarly, note the more uniform thickness, from medial to lateral, of the gluteus maximus muscle. The cryosection image presents a flat dorsal surface that conforms to the embedding substrate. Fatty regions, such as the superficial fascia of the rectus sheath, dorsolateral buttocks, anterior to the bladder, and perirectal fossa, are radiopaque. Acetabular, femoral, and sacral bony regions are brightest. Muscular and dermal layers are intermediate.

Cryosection. This section passes through the femoral head midway through the acetabulum. All three innominate bones (i.e., ilium, pubis, ischium) are seen in this section to form the acetabulum. The superiormost portion of the ventroflexors (sartorius and iliopsoas muscles) and lateral flexors (gluteus minimus, gluteus medius, and tensor fascia latae muscles) of the thigh are present. Since this level is superior to the inferior pubic ramus and the ischial tuberosity, the hamstring and lower limb adductor muscles are not seen. The femoral sheath surrounds structures of the subsartorial canal that pass under the inguinal ligament just superior to this level. Similarly, the spermatic cord enters the superficial ring of the inguinal canal just superior to this level.

Corresponding Magnetic Resonance (MR). In contrast to the CT image, this image highlights several clinically significant spaces defined by clear cartilaginous or ligamentous boundaries or both or by bright intermuscular septae. The femoral head capsule is fibrous and dark on this MR scan, whereas the vesicular (bladder) space, rectal fossa, anterior, lateral, and posterior muscular compartments are all highlighted by bright boundaries that are rich in fat content.

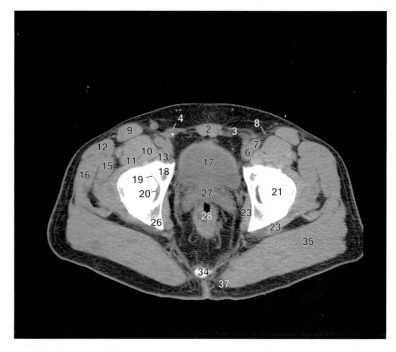

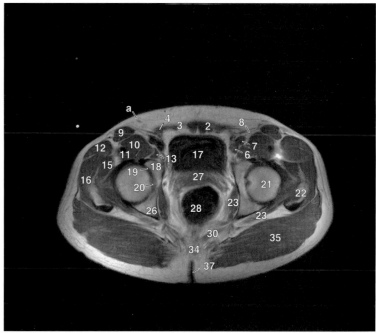

PLATE 5-2 LEFT THIGH: MID-DIAPHYSIS FEMUR *(Visible Man 2105)*

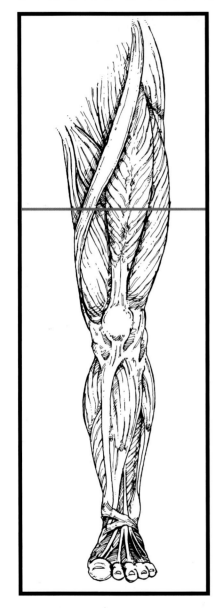

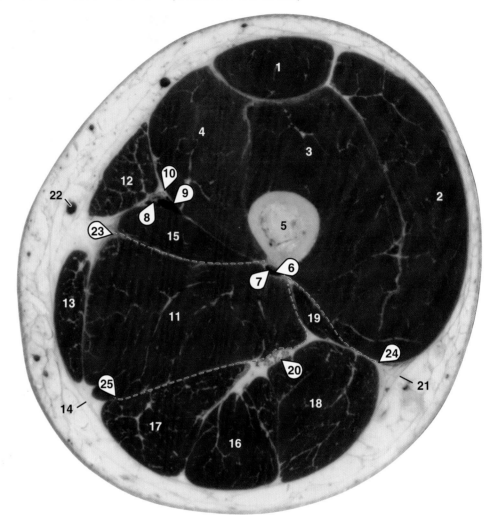

1	Rectus femoris muscle	13	Gracilis muscle	23	Anteriomedial intermuscular
2	Vastus lateralis muscle	14	Fascia lata		septum
3	Vastus intermedius muscle	15	Adductor longus muscle	24	Lateral intermuscular septum
4	Vastus medialis muscle	16	Semimembranosus muscle	25	Posteromedial intermuscular
5	Diaphysis of the left femur	17	Semitendinosus muscle		septum
6	Profunda femoris artery	18	Long head of the biceps femoris		
7	Profunda femoris vein		muscle		
8	Femoral artery	19	Short head of the biceps femoris		
9	Femoral vein		muscle		
10	Femoral nerve	20	Sciatic nerve		
11	Adductor magnus muscle	21	Iliotibial tract		
12	Sartorius muscle	22	Great saphenous vein		

RADIOGRAPHIC KEY

a   Lateral circumflex femoral artery
b   Medial circumflex femoral artery
c   Femoral artery
d   Descending branch of the
     profunda femoris artery

PLATE 5-2 LEFT THIGH: MID-DIAPHYSIS FEMUR *(Visible Man 2105)*

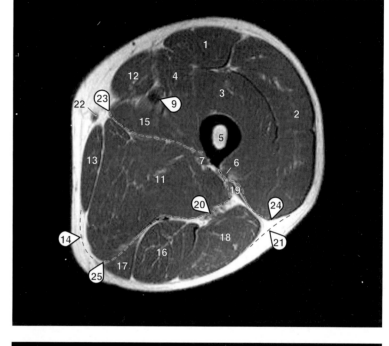

Corresponding MR. MR highlighting the fat in the subcutaneous, intramuscular, and marrow regions. Flow enhances the arterial blood vessels (brighter) over the venous channels. Note that in this living subject muscle tonus on the iliotibial tract raises the lateral margin of the thigh compared with the cryosection image. The medial flatness is caused by apposition with the opposing thigh (not seen).

Cryosection. Division of the upper and the middle half of the left femoral shaft. The anterior compartment is bounded posteriorly by the anteromedial and the lateral intermuscular septa. The investing fascia of the sartorius muscle must slide over the anterior compartment, thus it is not in one of the three femoral muscular compartments. It contains the quadriceps muscles, which receive motor supply from the femoral nerve. The adductor compartment is bound by the anteromedial and the posteromedial intermuscular septa. At this level it includes the adductor longus, gracilis, and adductor magnus muscles. The pectineus and adductor brevis insert onto the femur superior to this level. Except for the pectineus (femoral nerve) and the hamstring portion of the adductor magnus, all these muscles are innervated by the obturator nerve. The posterior compartment contains the hamstrings, all of which receive branches of the sciatic nerve. Of the three intermuscular septa, the lateral, which anchors the iliotibial tract, is the most robust.

Diagnostic Image. Diagnostic MR angiographic image of the femoral artery and its branches. The descending branch of the lateral circumflex femoral artery is most clearly seen on the right side where it becomes the superior lateral geniculate artery.

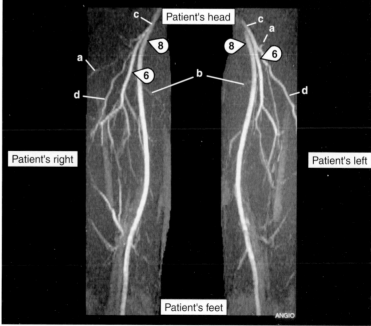

PLATE 5-3 SUPERIOR LEFT KNEE *(Visible Man 2273)*

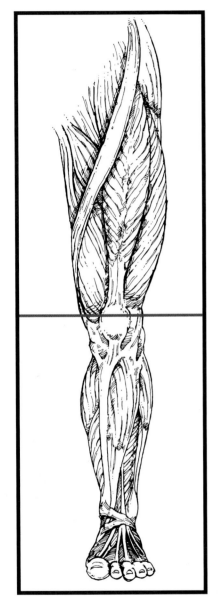

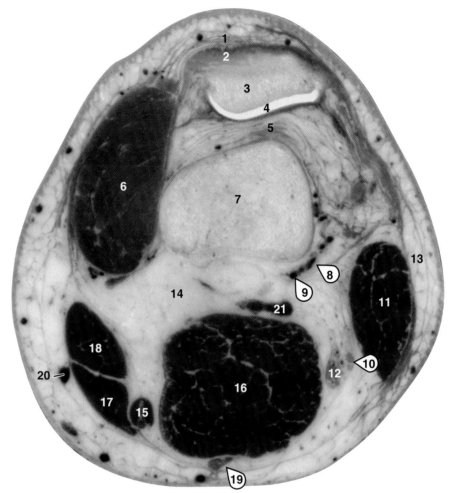

1	Prepatellar bursa	10	Common peroneal nerve
2	Patellar tendon	11	Biceps femoris muscle
3	Patella	12	Tibial nerve
4	Articular cartilage of the patella	13	Iliotibial tract
5	Suprapatellar (quadriceps) bursa	14	Popliteal fossa
6	Vastus medialis muscle	15	Adductor magnus muscle
7	Femur	16	Semimembranosus muscle
8	Popliteal vein	17	Gracilis muscle tendon
9	Popliteal artery	

18	Sartorius muscle
19	Semitendinosus muscle tendon
20	Great saphenous vein
21	Left head of the gastrocnemius muscle

RADIOGRAPHIC KEY

a   Capsule of the knee joint

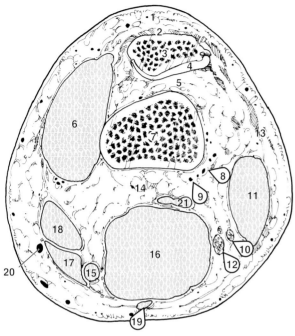

PLATE 5-3 SUPERIOR LEFT KNEE *(Visible Man 2273)*

Corresponding CT. CT highlighting the bone, muscular, some blood vessels, and some nerve components of the knee. Only the quadriceps tendon, and none of the patella, is visible. Note the patency of the popliteal artery and vein in this live subject.

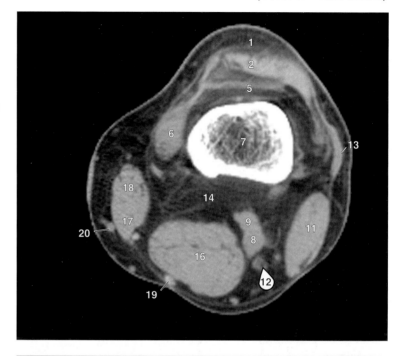

Cryosection. This section passes through the inferior femoral shaft just superior to the distal femoral condyles. The prepatellar and suprapatellar bursae are seen to surround the patella. These and several other bursae allow the patella to slide over the femoral condyles. The patellar tendon is seen as a cartilaginous layer anterior to the patella. The portion of the vastus medialis seen here is often referred to as the articularis genus muscle. It assists in maintaining the position of the suprapatellar bursa. The popliteal artery is collapsed and also appears to have a thickening of its lumen, perhaps atherosclerosis, which is common in this region. Note that the lateral portion of the gastrocnemius muscle has a higher point of origin than the medial portion that is found inferior to this level.

Corresponding MR. MR highlighting the fatty components of the knee. The capsular space of the knee is more discernible than in CT. Note the articular cartilage of the patella. (Key: A, anterior; L, left; P, posterior; M, medial.)

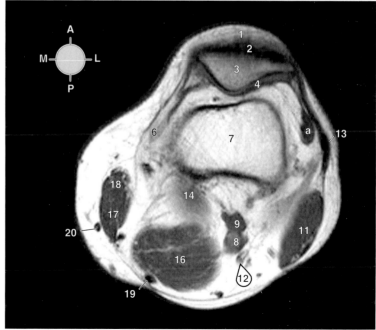

PLATE 5-4 LEFT MIDKNEE *(Visible Man 2325)*

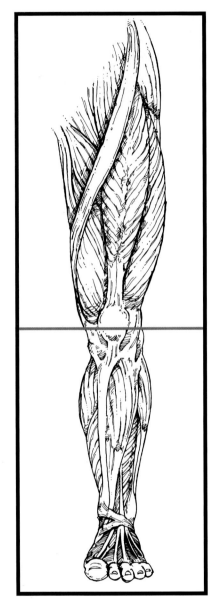

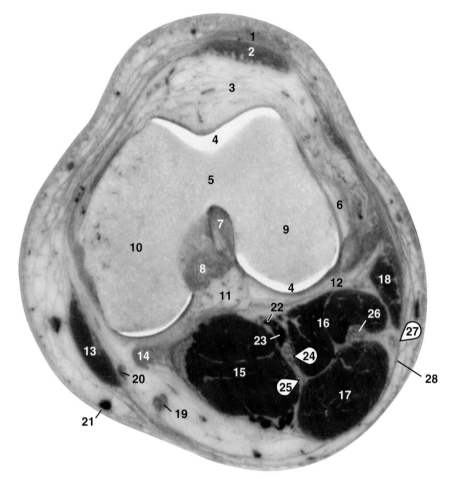

1	Prepatellar bursa	14	Semimembranosus muscle tendon	24	Tibial nerve
2	Patellar tendon			25	Medial sural cutaneous nerve
3	Suprapatellar (quadriceps) bursa	15	Medial head of the gastrocnemius muscle	26	Common peroneal nerve
4	Articular cartilage of the femur			27	Sural communicating nerve
5	Femur	16	Plantaris muscle	28	Iliotibial tract
6	Articular capsule	17	Lateral head of the gastrocnemius muscle		
7	Anterior cruciate ligament				

RADIOGRAPHIC KEY

8	Posterior cruciate ligament	18	Biceps femoris muscle	a	Patella
9	Lateral condyle of the femur	19	Semitendinosus muscle tendon	b	Patellar fat pad
10	Medial condyle of the femur	20	Gracilis muscle tendon	c	Quadriceps muscle tendon
11	Popliteal fossa	21	Great saphenous vein	d	Popliteus muscle
12	Gastrocnemius bursa	22	Popliteal artery	e	Tibia
13	Sartorius muscle	23	Popliteal vein		

PLATE 5-4 LEFT MIDKNEE *(Visible Man 2325)*

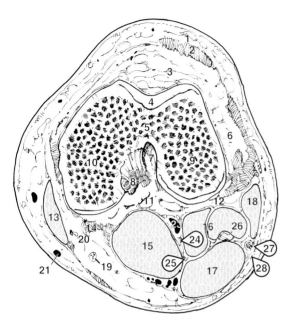

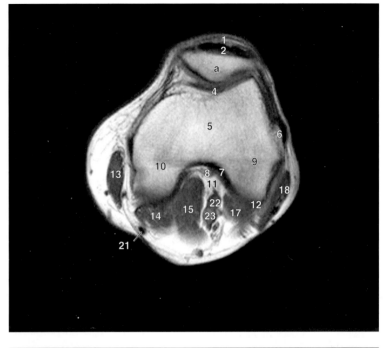

Corresponding MR. MR highlighting the fatty components of the knee. Note that the gracilis tendon appears dark. The patella is visible. Note the bright fat surrounding structures and also within the bone marrow of the femur and patella.

Cryosection. This section passes through the medial and lateral femoral condyles. The suprapatellar bursa can be seen to extend posteriorly around the lateral surface of the femur at this level. The gastrocnemius bursa protects that muscle during knee movements. The sural communicating branch of the common peroneal nerve joins the medial sural communicating nerve to form the sural nerve. This union usually occurs in the inferior half of the calf, but it can occur anywhere between that level and this one. Both cruciate ligaments are seen in this view. Their names refer to the relative position of their tibial attachment sites.

Diagnostic MR. Plane cutting through a medial parasagittal plane of the knee that presents both cruciate ligaments. The MR pulse sequence make fat bright, muscle intermediate, and fibrous tendons or ligaments dark in signal. This view is very helpful in evaluating for cruciate ligament injury. Note the suprapatellar bursa is collapsed in its normal state.

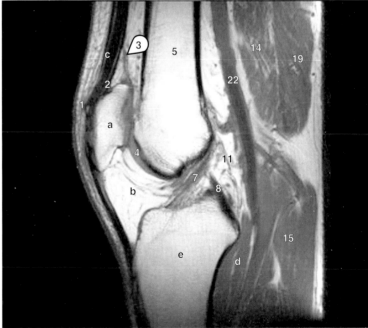

PLATE 5-5 LOWER LEFT KNEE *(Visible Man 2330)*

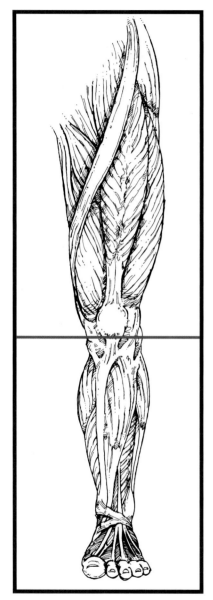

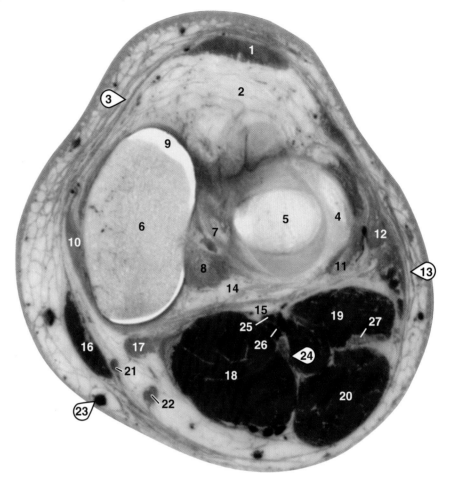

1 Patellar ligament	**14** Popliteal fossa	**24** Tibial nerve
2 Suprapatellar (quadriceps) bursa	**15** Gastrocnemius bursa	**25** Popliteal artery
3 Articular capsule	**16** Sartorius muscle	**26** Popliteal vein
4 Lateral meniscus	**17** Semimembranosus muscle tendon	**27** Common peroneal nerve
5 Lateral condyle of the femur	**18** Medial head of the gastrocnemius muscle	**RADIOGRAPHIC KEY**
6 Medial condyle of the femur	**19** Plantaris muscle	**a** Biceps femoris muscle
7 Anterior cruciate ligament	**20** Lateral head of the gastrocnemius muscle	**b** Femur
8 Posterior cruciate ligament		**c** Tibial collateral ligament
9 Articular cartilage of the femur	**21** Gracilis muscle tendon	**d** Medial meniscus
10 Medial collateral ligament	**22** Semitendinosus muscle tendon	**e** Tibia
11 Popliteus muscle tendon	**23** Great saphenous vein	**f** Intercondylar eminence
12 Lateral collateral ligament		
13 Iliotibial tract		

PLATE 5-5 LOWER LEFT KNEE *(Visible Man 2330)*

Corresponding MR. Again note the bright fatty tissue and how clearly it delineates various structures. Ligaments and tendons are dark. Note the differentiation between the grocilis tendon and semimembraneous muscle.

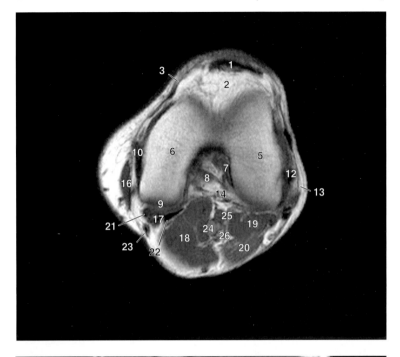

Cryosection. This section passes through the medial and the lateral femoral condyles and the circular lateral meniscus of the left tibial plateau. The lateral and the medial collateral ligaments are visible. The separation of the lateral collateral ligament from the lateral meniscus is apparent, unlike when the medial collateral ligament is attached to the medial meniscus. Medially, we see the characteristic anteroposterior alignment of the sartorius, gracilis, and semitendinosus tendons. Their three pronged alignment on the medial surface of the knee is often referred to as the pes anserinus (from the Latin for goose's foot).

Diagnostic MR. Coronal MR image of the left knee. The medial and lateral menisci appear as dark triangular spaces at either side of the knee joint. Note that the medial meniscus is continuous with the medial collateral ligament. Thus the medial meniscus is at risk during the unnatural lateral flexion (i.e., trauma) of the knee and the ancillary stretching of medial collateral ligament. The lateral meniscus is a separate structure from the lateral collateral ligament and is less at risk during unnatural medial flexion of the knee. Note the gray articular cartilage along the femoral condyles and tibial plateau. Orientation: S, superior; M, medial; I, inferior; L, lateral.

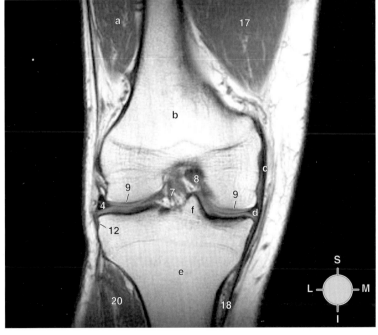

PLATE 5-6 LEFT CALF: UPPER DIAPHYSIS TIBIA AND FIBULA *(Visible Man 2373)*

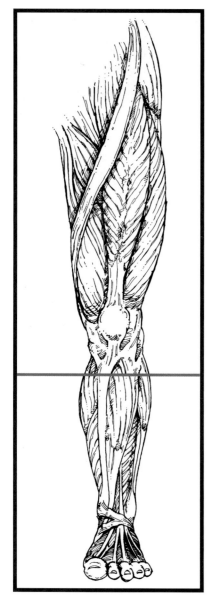

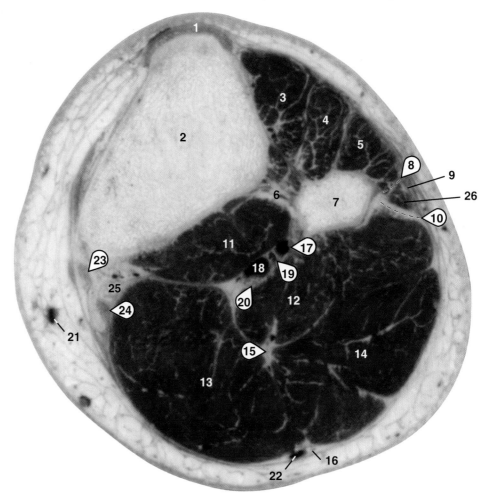

1 Patellar tendon	**13** Medial head of the gastrocnemius muscle	**24** Semitendinosus muscle tendon
2 Tibia		**25** Semimembranosus muscle tendon
3 Tibialis anterior muscle	**14** Lateral head of the gastrocnemius muscle	**26** Peroneus longus muscle
4 Extensor digitorum muscle		
5 Peroneus longus muscle	**15** Plantaris muscle tendon	## RADIOGRAPHIC KEY
6 Interosseous membrane	**16** Sural nerve	**a** Diaphysis of the femur
7 Fibula	**17** Peroneal artery	**b** Epiphyseal plate of the femur
8 Anterior crural septum	**18** Posterior tibial artery	**c** Epiphysis of the femur
9 Superficial peroneal nerve	**19** Posterior tibial vein	**d** Epiphysis of the tibia
10 Posterior crural septum	**20** Tibial nerve	**e** Epiphyseal plate of the tibia
11 Tibialis posterior muscle	**21** Great saphenous vein	**f** Diaphysis of the tibia
12 Soleus muscle	**22** Small saphenous vein	**g** Proximal tibiofibular joint
	23 Gracilis muscle tendon	

PLATE 5·6 LEFT CALF: UPPER DIAPHYSIS TIBIA AND FIBULA *(Visible Man 2373)*

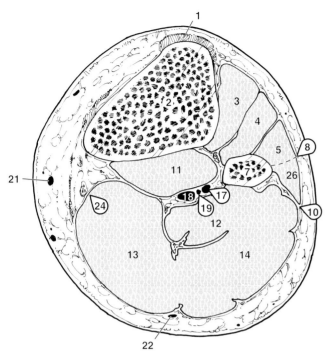

Corresponding MR. Axial MR highlighting the fatty components of the upper calf. Therefore, the tibial and fibular marrow cavities appear much brighter than their compact bone cortices. Vessels appear as lucencies. The investing fascia and intramuscular septa surrounding each muscle are better visualized than in a CT or a plain-film radiograph.

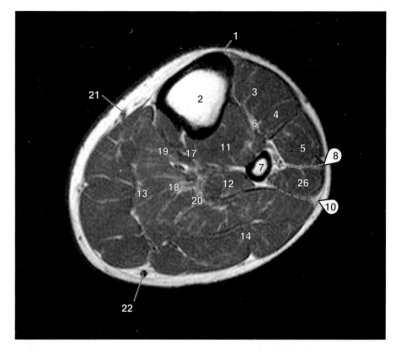

Cryosection. This section passes through the proximal tibia and fibula, just inferior to the tibial plateau. At this level two tiny intermuscular septa, the interosseous membrane and the anterior crural septum, separate posteriorly, bound by the anterior muscular compartment. The lateral compartment is bound by the anterior and the posterior crural septae. The posterior compartment is bound by the interosseous membrane and the posterior crural septum. At this level only the triceps surae (i.e., the two heads of the gastrocnemius and soleus muscles) and tibialis posterior are visible.

Diagnostic Plain-Film Radiograph. Posterior-anterior radiograph from a child's knee. Note that the epiphyseal plates of the femur and tibia are not yet fused in this child and are lucent. The epiphyseal plate is made of cartilage, which is not completely mineralized and not as dense as fully mineralized bone. (Key: S, superior; M, medial; D, dorsal; L, left.)

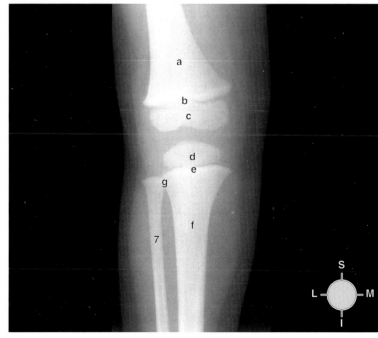

PLATE 5-7 LEFT CALF: LOWER DIAPHYSIS TIBIA AND FIBULA *(Visible Man 2551)*

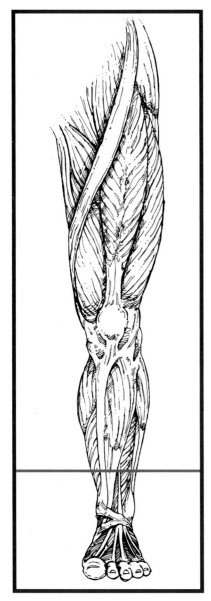

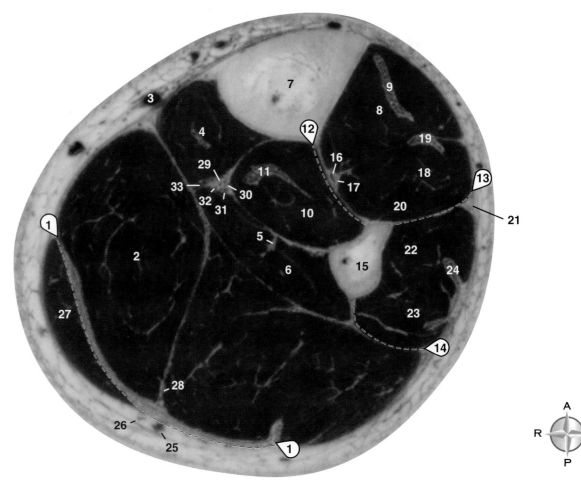

1 Thickened outer investing layer of the soleus muscle fascia	**14** Posterior crural septum	**27** Gastrocnemius muscle
2 Soleus muscle	**15** Fibula	**28** Plantaris muscle tendon
3 Great saphenous vein	**16** Anterior tibial artery	**29** Tibial nerve
4 Flexor digitorum longus muscle	**17** Anterior tibial vein	**30** Peroneal artery
5 Flexor hallucis longus muscle tendon	**18** Extensor digitorum longus muscle	**31** Peroneal vein
6 Flexor hallucis longus muscle	**19** Extensor digitorum longus muscle tendon	**32** Posterior tibial artery
7 Tibia	**20** Extensor hallicus longus muscle	**33** Posterior tibial vein
8 Tibialis anterior muscle	**21** Superficial peroneal nerve	
9 Tibialis anterior muscle tendon	**22** Peroneus brevis muscle	## RADIOGRAPHIC KEY
10 Tibialis posterior muscle	**23** Peroneus longus muscle	**a** Posterior tibial vessels
11 Tibialis posterior muscle tendon	**24** Peroneus longus muscle tendon	**b** Medial head of the gastrocnemius muscle
12 Interosseous membrane	**25** Small saphenous vein	**c** Medial head of the gastrocnemius muscle
13 Anterior crural septum	**26** Sural nerve	

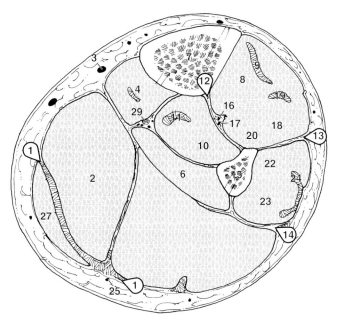

Corresponding CT. The flattened posterior surface owes to this individuals' supine posture while in the CT scanner. This surface would be more rounded if they were in an orthograde position. Compared with Plate 5-6, this more distal tibial cross section shows less right-left width and greater anteroposterior depth.

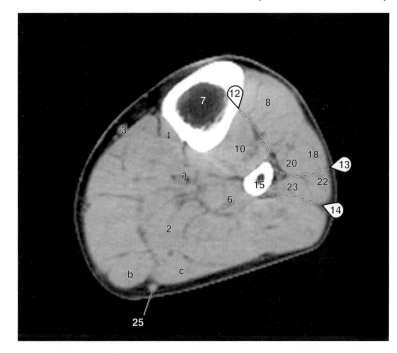

Cryosection. Axial section that passes between the upper 2/3 and lower 1/3 of the calf or shank (the anatomical leg). The anterior, crural (lateral), and posterior muscular compartments are clearly defined. The large muscle tendons of the tibialis posterior, tibialis anterior, and peroneus longus muscles are present. Whereas the superficial posterior muscular compartment in Plate 5-6 is primarily gastrocnemius muscle, this more inferior section finds this compartment mainly composed of the soleus muscle body. The broad portion of the tibial diaphysis has no muscular or tendinous covering anteriorly and is thus subcutaneous at this level.

Corresponding MR. Muscles of all compartments appear larger and more rounded than in the corresponding CT image. The proportions and shapes of the anterior, lateral, and posterior compartments are most similar to the Visible Man cryosection image. Note the clarity of the clear (appear to be spaces) intermuscular septae, blood vessels, and tendons. Note that the superficial fascial space (containing fat that appears bright in this MR image) is thickest medially and posteriorly in all three images.

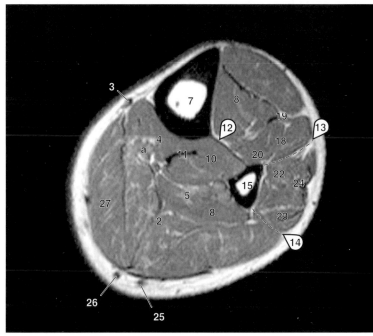

PLATE 5-8 LEFT DISTAL CALF: TIBIOFIBULAR JOINT *(Visible Man 2715)*

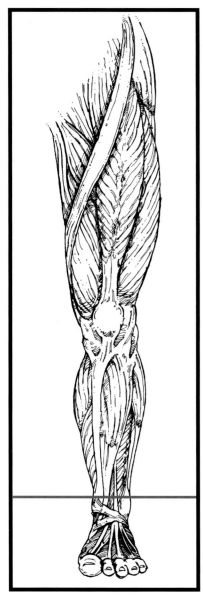

1 Tibia
2 Tibialis anterior muscle tendon
3 Extensor hallucis longus muscle and tendon
4 Anterior tibial vein
5 Anterior tibial artery
6 Peroneus tertius muscle
7 Extensor digitorum longus muscle tendon
8 Fibula
9 Superior extensor retinaculum
10 Tibialis posterior muscle tendon
11 Flexor digitorum longus muscle tendon
12 Flexor hallucis longus muscle and tendon
13 Peroneus brevis muscle
14 Peroneus longus muscle tendon
15 Sural nerve
16 Tendo calcaneus (Achilles) tendon
17 Plantaris muscle tendon
18 Small saphenous vein
19 Inferior tibiofibular joint
20 Posterior tibial vein
21 Posterior tibial artery
22 Tibial nerve

RADIOGRAPHIC KEY

a Peroneal artery
b Peroneus tertius muscle
c Peroneal vein

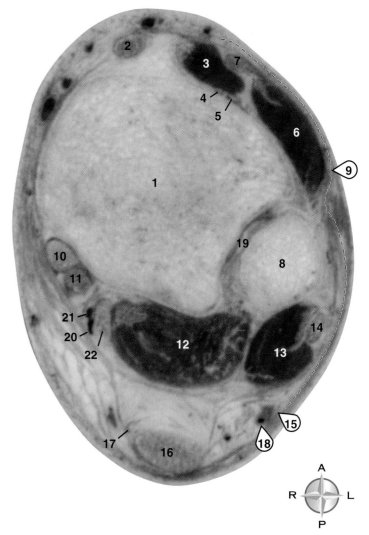

PLATE 5-8 LEFT DISTAL CALF: TIBIOFIBULAR JOINT (*Visible Man 2715*)

Corresponding CT. CT highlighting the bone and the muscular components of the upper calf. The entire bone in this region appears bright and, apparently, dense. All significant blood vessels and nerves appear as opacities. The tendo calcaneus bursa is not demonstrated well since it is collapsed.

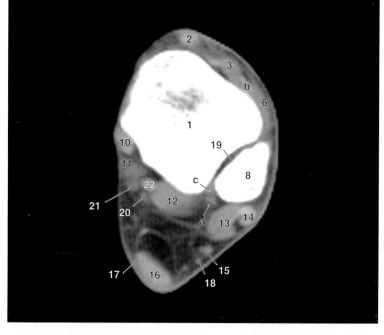

Cryosection. This section passes through the distal tibiofibular joint, just superior to the upper ankle joint. The superior extensor retinaculum prevents bowstringing of muscles and tendons in the lateral and anterior compartments during extension (dorsiflexion) of the foot. The tendo calcaneus bursa prevents friction between the tendo calcaneus tendon and muscles and the deep muscles and tendons of the posterior crural compartment.

Diagnostic Image. MR of the distal tibia and fibula just above the ankle shows bright fat around the tendons surrounding the ankle. Note a small amount of bright synovial fluid in the tibiofibular joint.

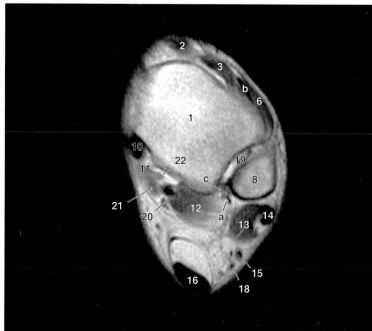

PLATE 5-9 LEFT UPPER ANKLE JOINT *(Visible Man 2731)*

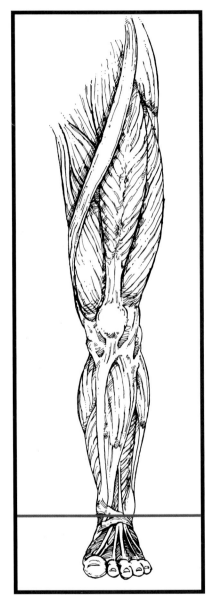

1 Anterior tibial artery
2 Anterior tibial vein
3 Tibialis anterior muscle
4 Inferior extensor retinaculum
5 Great saphenous vein
6 Extensor digitorum longus muscle
7 Extensor digitorum longus muscle tendon
8 Superficial peroneal nerve
9 Peroneus tertius muscle
10 Peroneus tertius muscle tendon
11 Medial malleolus of the tibia
12 Talus
13 Lateral malleolus of the fibula
14 Upper ankle joint
15 Tibialis posterior muscle tendon
16 Flexor digitorum longus muscle
17 Posterior tibial artery
18 Posterior tibial artery venae comitantes
19 Tibial nerve
20 Peroneus brevis muscle
21 Peroneus brevis muscle tendon
22 Peroneus longus muscle tendon
23 Tendo calcaneus bursa
24 Tendo calcaneus fat pad
25 Tendo calcaneus tendon
26 Plantaris muscle tendon
27 Flexor hallucis longus muscle
28 Flexor hallucis longus muscle tendon
29 Small saphenous vein

RADIOGRAPHIC KEY

a Tibia
b Fracture
c Calcaneus
d Navicular
e Cuboid
f Medial cuneiform
g Intermediate cuneiform
h First metatarsal
i Second metatarsal

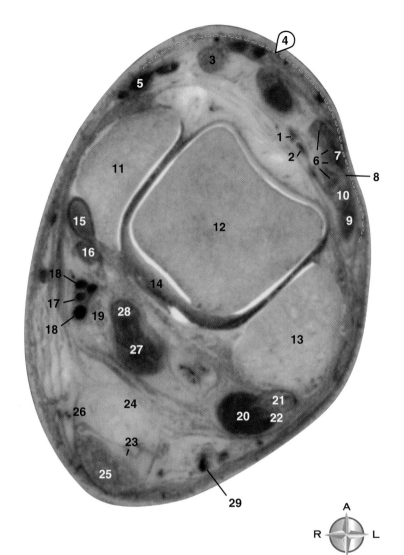

PLATE 5-9 LEFT UPPER ANKLE JOINT *(Visible Man 2731)*

Corresponding CT. Tendons and vessels are packed either anteriorly or posteriorly around the upper ankle joint. The distal tibia and fibula are tightly bound. The malleoli are tightly bound to the foot. The motion at this joint is highly directed about a dorsoplantar axis. However, the subcutaneous malleoli are vulnerable to medial and lateral forces and especially to foreign-body impact. If one malleolus breaks on lateral or medial impact, the amount of force then needed to break the other and to keep driving the calf off the foot is greatly reduced.

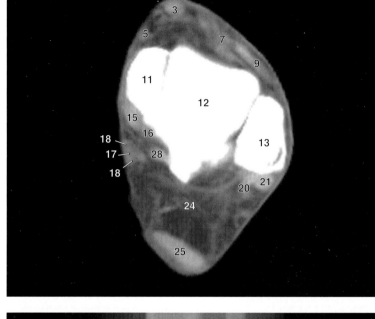

Cryosection. This section passes through the upper ankle joint, separating the calf or shank (anatomical leg) from the foot. The maximum amount of dorsiflexion and plantar flexion of the foot can occur at this joint. Note the groove behind the tibia that guides the tibialis posterior and the flexor digitorum longus muscle tendons into the foot. Similarly, the inferior extensor retinaculum prevents the tendons of anterior compartment muscles from bowstringing during dorsiflexion of the foot.

Diagnostic Plain-Film Radiograph. The medial malleolus of the tibia is strongly bound to the navicular, calcaneus, and talus bones by the deltoid ligament. Similarly, the lateral malleolus of the fibula has ligamentous bindings to the talus and calcaneus. Moreover, the distal tibia and fibula are tightly bound. During extreme eversion, the strong deltoid may hold better than the distalmost fibula (lateral malleolus). Fracture of the lateral malleolus during eversion of the foot places the entire load of the body on the medial malleolus, perhaps completing a fracture of both malleoli, a condition referred to as Pott's fracture. Note the transverse fracture of the medial malleolus and oblique fracture of the distal fibula.

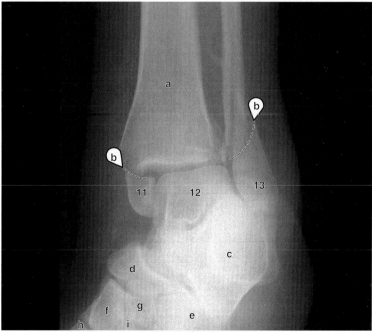

PLATE 5-10 LEFT LOWER (SUBTALAR) ANKLE JOINT *(Visible Man 2755)*

1 Great saphenous vein
2 Saphenous nerve
3 Dorsalis pedis artery
4 Lateral process of the talus
5 Tibialis anterior muscle tendon
6 Extensor hallicus longus muscle tendon
7 Extensor digitorum brevis muscle
8 Extensor digitorum longus muscle tendon
9 Peroneus tertius muscle tendon
10 Talocalcaneaonavicular joint
11 Talocalcaneus ligament
12 Head of the talus
13 Talocalcaneal (subtalar) joint
14 Talocalcaneal (subtalar) joint capsule
15 Peroneus brevis muscle tendon
16 Peroneus longus muscle tendon
17 Calcaneus
18 Tendo calcaneus tendon
19 Lateral plantar nerve
20 Posterior tibial artery venae comitantes
21 Posterior tibial artery
22 Medial plantar nerve
23 Flexor hallucis longus muscle tendon
24 Flexor hallucis longus muscle
25 Flexor digitorum muscle tendon
26 Tibialis posterior muscle tendon
27 Sustentaculum tali

RADIOGRAPHIC KEY

a Fibula
b Tibia
c Fracture
d Tuber calcanei
e Talus
f Navicular
g Cuboid
h Lateral cuneiform
i Intermediate cuneiform
j Tuberosity of the fifth metatarsal
m Metatarsals followed by the corresponding number

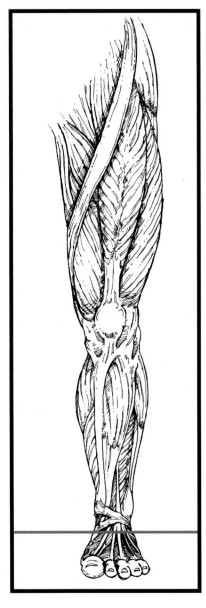

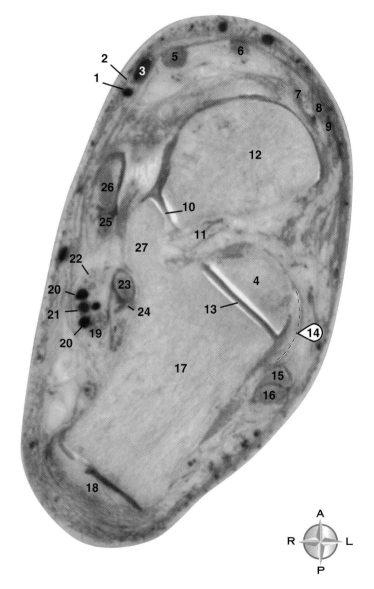

PLATE 5-10 LEFT LOWER (SUBTALAR) ANKLE JOINT *(Visible Man 2755)*

Corresponding CT. A large calcaneal tendon (tendo calcaneus) is seen below a thin covering of skin. The approximation of the flexor digitorum longus, the tibialis posterior muscle tendons, and the medial portion of the talus is more apparent than in the cryosection image. Grooves for the two peroneal muscle tendons are also more apparent on this image. Anterior compartment tendons appear appressed to the anterior aspect of the talus underneath a retinaculum with thin-skin overlying. This is more characteristic of this area *in vivo* than the Visible Man cryosection image.

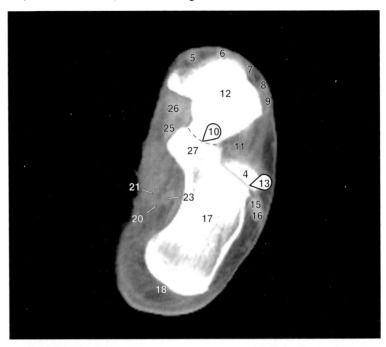

Cryosection. Axial section that passes through the left lower ankle joint. Also called the talocalcaneus or subtalar joint, it is the primary contact between the talus and the calcaneus. The well-developed subtalar joint capsule is seen on the lateral surface of this joint. Motion is seen here during inversion and eversion of the foot. Note that the flexor digitorum longus muscle tendon grooves the back of the sustentaculum tali, a medial process of the calcaneus that supports the talus superiorly. The tendo calcaneus is seen to insert onto the posterior aspect of the calcaneal tuberosity. The tibial nerve divides into the medial and the lateral plantar nerves. The posterior tibial artery divides more distally in this individual.

Diagnostic Plain-Film Radiograph. Medial-to-lateral plain-film radiograph of a foot where the tendo calcaneus has avulsed, carrying a portion of the superior surface of the calcaneal tuberosity with it.

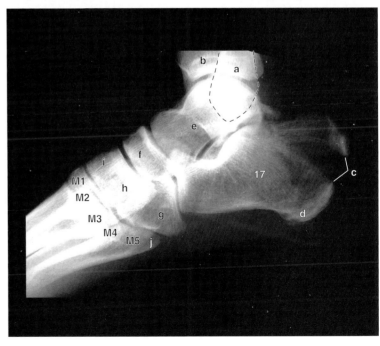

PLATE 5-11 LEFT MIDDISTAL TARSAL BONES *(Visible Man Replanarized Foot #1)*

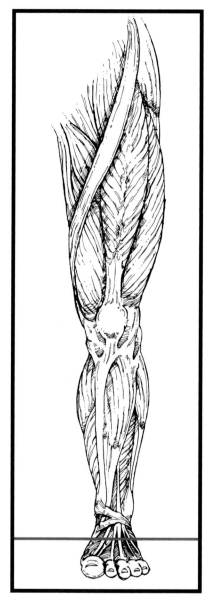

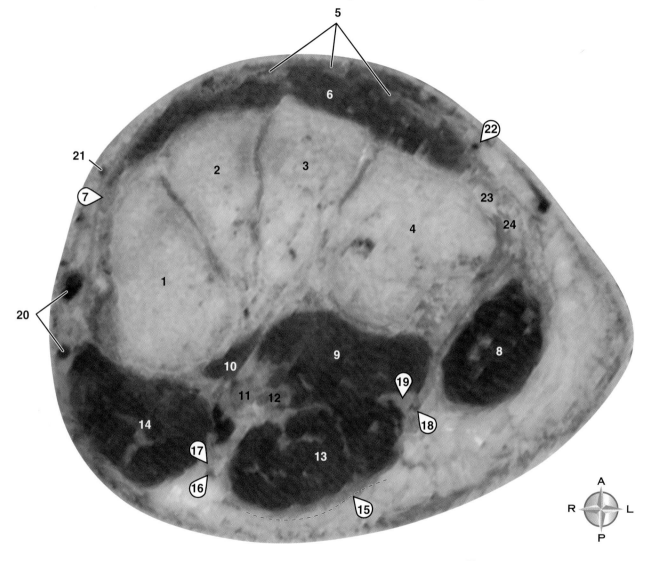

1 Medial cuneiform
2 Intermediate cuneiform
3 Lateral cuneiform
4 Cuboid
5 Extensor digitorum longus muscle
   tendon

6   Extensor digitorum brevis muscle
7   Extensor hallucis longus tendon
8   Abductor digiti minimi muscle
9   Quadratus plantae muscle
10 Flexor hallucis brevis muscle
11 Flexor hallucis longus muscle tendon
12 Flexor digitorum longus tendon
13 Flexor digitorum brevis muscle
14 Abductor hallucis muscle

15 Plantar aponeurosis
16 Medial plantar artery
17 Medial plantar nerve
18 Lateral plantar artery
19 Lateral plantar nerve
20 Medial tarsal artery
21 Dorsalis pedis artery
22 Lateral tarsal artery
23 Tibialis anterior muscle tendon
24 Tibialis posterior muscle tendon

RADIOGRAPHIC KEY

a Tibia
b Fibula
c Talus
d Fracture
e Navicular
f Cuboid
g Lateral cuneiform
h Tuberosity of the fifth metatarsal

PLATE 5-11 LEFT MIDDISTAL TARSAL BONES *(Visible Man Replanarized Foot #1)*

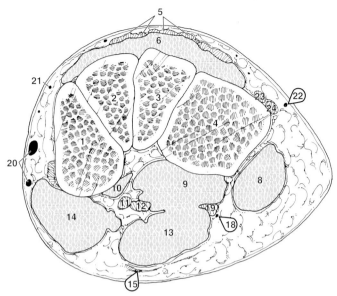

Corresponding CT. CT highlighting the bony and muscular components of the foot. The posterior extension of this image shows that its orientation is more horizontal and less transverse (axial) than the replanarized cryosection image.

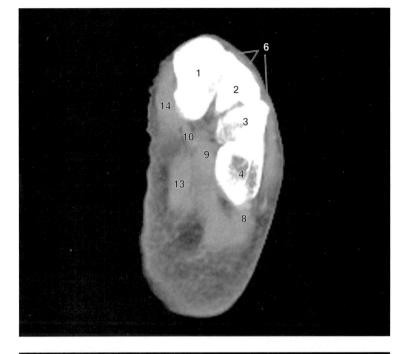

Cryosection. This section passes through the distal tarsal bones, just posterior (proximal) to the metatarsals and just distal to the midtarsal joint (i.e., calcaneocuboid and talonavicular joints). Both the tibialis posterior and anterior muscles are seen to insert on the tarsal bones in this plane. The flexor digitorum longus tendons spread out just anterior to this plane, providing origin for the lumbrical muscles.

Diagnostic Plain-Film Radiograph. Lateral-to-medial plain-film radiograph of the proximal foot. This image presents a fracture of the talus.

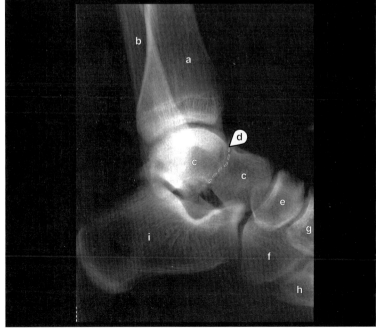

PLATE 5-12 LEFT MIDMETATARSALS *(Visible Man Replanarized Foot #2)*

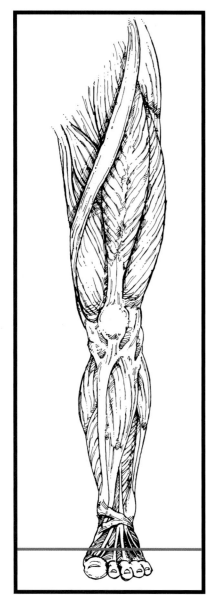

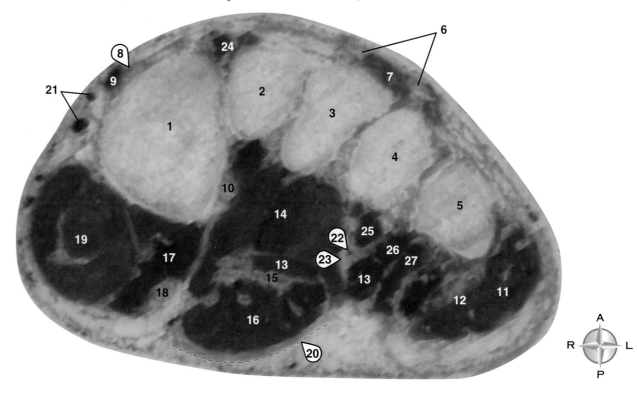

1	First metatarsal	
2	Second metatarsal	
3	Third metatarsal	
4	Fourth metatarsal	
5	Fifth metatarsal	
6	Extensor digitorum longus muscle tendon	
7	Dorsal interossei muscle	
8	Extensor hallucis longus tendon	
9	First dorsal metatarsal artery	
10	Peroneus longus muscle tendon	
11	Abductor digiti minimi muscle	
12	Flexor digiti minimi muscle	
13	Lumbrical muscle	
14	Oblique abductor hallucis brevis muscle	

15 Flexor digitorum longus tendon
16 Flexor digitorum brevis muscle
17 Flexor hallucis brevis muscle
18 Flexor hallucis longus tendon
19 Abductor hallucis muscle
20 Plantar aponeurosis
21 Dorsal digital artery
22 Lateral plantar artery
23 Lateral plantar vein
24 Extensor hallucis brevis muscle
25 First plantar interosseous muscle
26 Second plantar interosseous muscle
27 Third plantar interosseous muscle

RADIOGRAPHIC KEY

a Tibia
b Calcaneus
c Navicular
d Cuboid
e Medial cuneiform
f Intermediate cuneiform
g Lateral cuneiform
h Sesmoids
i Fracture
j Talus
k Fibula
M Metatarsals followed by the corresponding number
P Proximal phalanges followed by the corresponding number

PLATE 5-12 LEFT MIDMETATARSALS *(Visible Man Replanarized Foot #2)*

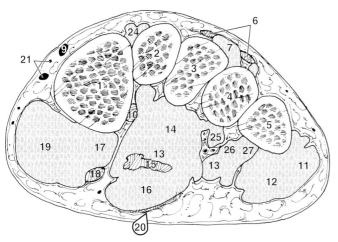

Cryosection. This section passes through the heads of the metatarsal bones. The strong plantar aponeurosis is seen to span the abductor digiti minimi and the abductor hallucis. Both portions of the adductor pollicis are seen. Many of the dorsal and plantar interossei and two lumbrical muscles are seen.

Corresponding CT. CT highlighting the bony and muscular components of the distal foot. Note that this live individual has a lower transverse arch, visible on the plantar surface of the foot. Because of the obliquity of this primarily axial section, the plantar aponeurosis appears thicker than it likely is.

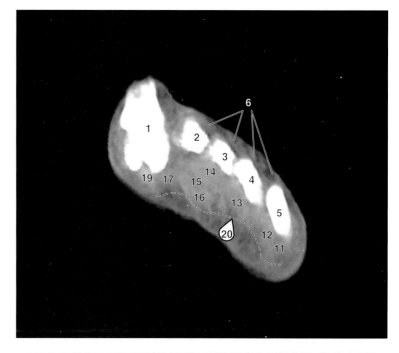

Diagnostic Plain-Film Radiograph. Dorsal-to-plantar radiograph of the right foot. Note the two sesamoid bones in the flexor hallucis brevis tendons framing the flexor hallucis longus tendon. The three medial metatarsals (2–4) show distal fractures.

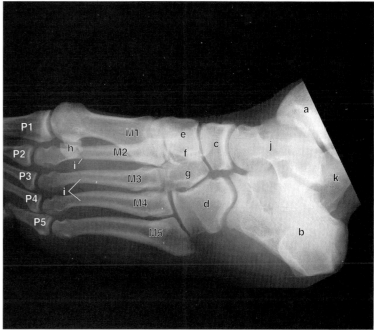

CHAPTER 6

Back

INTRODUCTION

Plates 6-1 and 6-2 show the back muscles that extend into the neck region, including the suboccipital triangle, erector spinae, and the prevertebral compartment muscles. The superiormost extent of the dorsal muscles is the nuchal line. The semispinalis and the longissimus portions of the erector spinae group of primarily lower-back and midback muscles extend to the base of the skull inferior to the nuchal line. The cervical vertebral column is seen in plain-film radiographs (Figs. 6-1 to 6-5). The cervical vertebrae have the most variable morphology of the five vertebral segments (e.g., cervical, thoracic, lumbar, sacral, and coccygeal).

The transition from neck to thorax is seen in Plates 6-2 and 6-3 in the morphology of the vertebral spines and the appearance of ribs. The thoracic vertebral column and ribs bring about significantly reduced intervertebral movement through their interconnecting musculature and the inferiorly inclined spinous processes. For this reason thoracic intervertebral disc distension is less common than in the more mobile cervical and lumbar regions. For the same reason, osteoporosis in the thoracic region leads to a more frozen stoop, referred to as kyphosis. Permanent dorsal bending of the vertebral column is referred to as lordosis as opposed to lateral bending, which is referred to as scoliosis. Plate 6-4 also shows upper and lower back overlap in depicting both the trapezius and latissimus dorsi muscles.

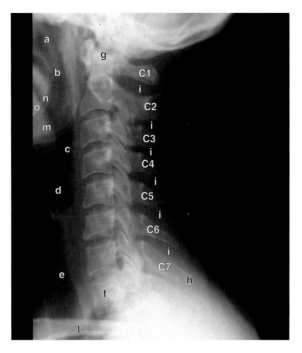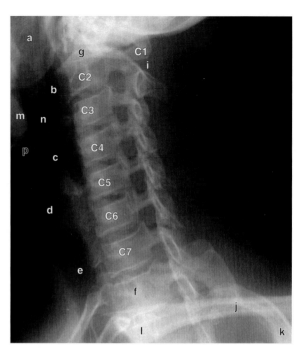

FIGURES 6-1–6-5 **Plain-Film Radiographs of the Cervical Vertebral Column (Neck).** Patient orientation in numerical order: left-to-right lateral, left-to-right 0.75 oblique, right-to-left 0.75 oblique, anterior-to-posterior coronal, left-to-right lateral with neck ventrally flexed. Key: a, nasopharynx; b, oropharynx; c, laryngopharynx; d, larynx; e, trachea; f, thoracic vertebra T1; g, dens epistrophe (odontoid process); h, spinous process of vertebra prominens (C7); i, ligamentum nuchae; j, clavicle; k, rib (1–3); l, manubrium; m, mandible; n, angle of the mandible; o, tongue; p, hyoid; q, epiglottis; and r, laryngeal cartilage. *(continued)*

A lumbar cross section is depicted in Plate 6-5. It is the site of the portion of the adult spinal cord, below the third lumbar vertebra, that typically includes only nerve roots within the subarachnoid space, the cauda equina. Lumbar puncture of the epidural space outside the lumbar cistern, a cerebrospinal fluid (CSF) filled space, is often attempted for pelvic and lower limb anesthesia between the spinous processes of lumbar vertebrae 3 and 4 while the patient's lower back is ventrally flexed. A sacral cross section is seen in Plate 6-6 in which the broad and ligamentously restrained iliosacral joint is depicted. Involved mainly in support of the pelvic floor (i.e., the anal and the urogenital triangles), the coccygeal vertebrae are rarely the target of tomographic imaging studies.

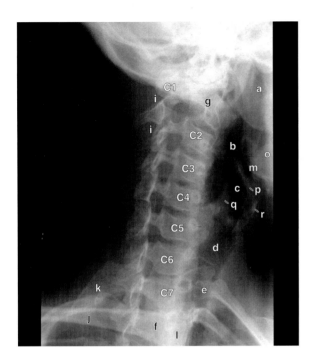
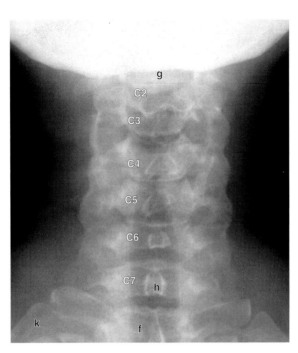
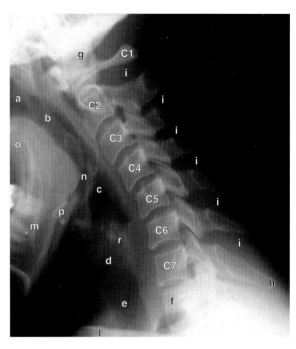

FIGURES 6-1–6-5 *(continued)* **Plain-Film Radiographs of the Cervical Vertebral Column (Neck).**   Patient orientation in numerical order: left-to-right lateral, left-to-right 0. 75 oblique, right-to-left 0.75 oblique, anterior-to-posterior coronal, left-to-right lateral with neck ventrally flexed. Key: a, nasopharynx; b, oropharynx; c, laryngopharynx; d, larynx; e, trachea; f, thoracic vertebra T1; g, dens epistrophe (odontoid process); h, spinous process of vertebra prominens (C7); i, ligamentum nuchae; j, clavicle; k, rib (1–3); l, manubrium; m, mandible; n, angle of the mandible; o, tongue; p, hyoid; q, epiglottis; and r, laryngeal cartilage.

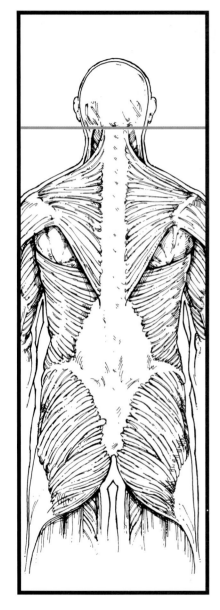

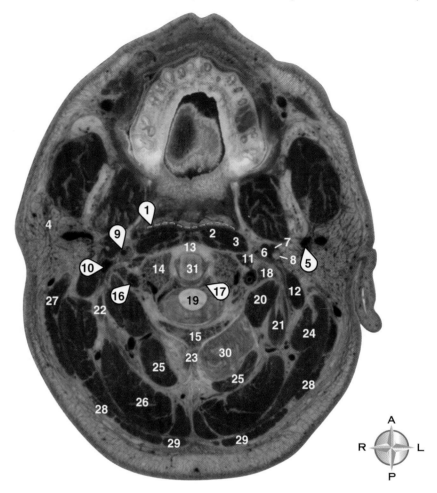

1   Alar prevertebral fascial planes
2   Longus colli muscle
3   Longus capitis muscle
4   Parotid gland
5   Retromandibular vein
6   Stylopharyngeus muscle
7   Styloglossus muscle
8   Stylohyoid muscle and ligament
9   Internal carotid artery
10 Internal jugular vein
11 Rectus capitis lateralis muscle
12 Posterior digastric muscle
13 Anterior arch of the "atlas" first
    cervical vertebra
14 Lateral mass of the atlas

15 Posterior arch of the atlas
16 Vertebral artery
17 Transverse ligament of the cruciform
    ligament
18 Transverse process of the atlas
19 Spinal cord
20 Rectus capitis posterior major muscle
21 Obliquus capitis inferior muscle
22 Obliquus capitis superioris muscle
23 Spinous process of the atlas
24 Longissimus capitis muscle
25 Rectus capitis posterior minor muscle
26 Semispinalis capitis muscle
27 Sternocleidomastoid muscle

28 Splenius capitis muscle
29 Trapezius muscle
30 Unidentified mass
31 Dens epistrophe

RADIOGRAPHIC KEY

a   Transverse foramen
b   External occipital protuberance
c   Cervical vertebra (corresponding
    number follows)
d   Digastric groove
e   Mastoid process
f   Zygomatic arch of the temporal bone
g   Mandible

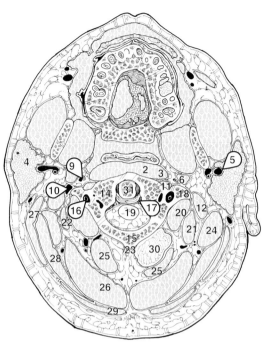

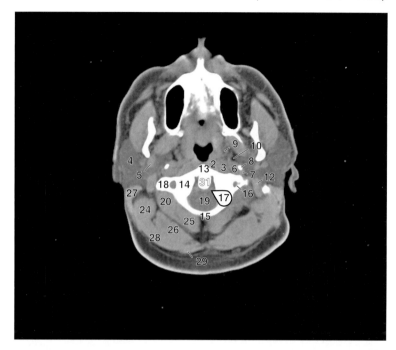

Corresponding Computed Tomography (CT). As with the cryosection, this section passes through the first cervical vertebra. Because this vertebra often has a small or no spinous process, the nuchal ligament may originate centrally on the posterior aspect of the vertebral arch. The sheetlike nuchal ligament would then have a long traverse between the right and the left side back musculature in the neck. The dens epistrophe is again clearly visualized in this section.

Cryosection. This section is not far inferior to the nuchal line (demarcating the scalp from the neck) made by the insertion of sternocleidomastoid, splenius capitis, and semispinalis capitis. The atlas (first cervical vertebra) has unusual features, such as no centrum (body), the transverse ligament (part of cruciform ligament) holding the dens epistrophe in place, foramina transversaria housing the vertebral arteries, lateral masses, and bifid spinous processes. Note that all four suboccipital muscles (rectus capitis posterior major, rectus capitis posterior minor, obliquus capitis superioris, and obliquus capitis inferioris) can be seen in this section.

Three-Dimensional (3D) CT. Adjacent CT slices, covering the approximately 30-cm height of the neck and head have been used to produce surface images of the skull alone. For most of the skull portion of the 3D CT volume to be quickly obtained, all CT image intensity values (pixel brightness) above a user-set threshold were chosen. Although this thresholding method may not obtain all the bone, it can insure that only bone is visualized. Such 3D renderings are often useful for visualizing disease processes or trauma that cut across somewhat thin CT slices. Three-dimensional renderings may be particularly useful for volume assessments and for surgical planning. Here the skull and cervical spine are seen from posterior view.

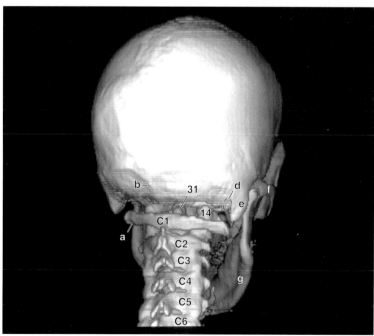

PLATE 6-2 LOWER NUCHAL MUSCULATURE *(Visible Man 1248)*

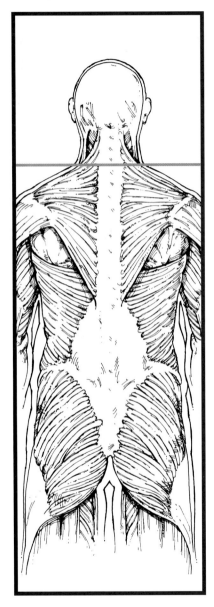

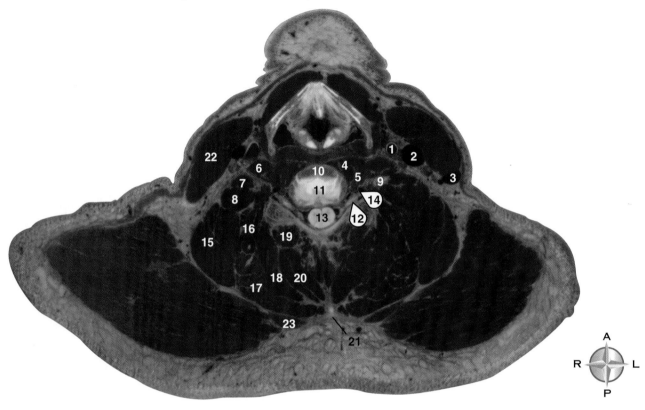

1 Common carotid artery	**11** Intervertebral disc between the fourth and the fifth vertebrae	**21** Ligamentum nuchae
2 Internal jugular vein		**22** Sternocleidomastoid muscle
3 External jugular vein	**12** Dorsal root ganglion	**23** Rhomboid minor muscle
4 Longus capitis muscle	**13** Spinal cord	
5 Longus colli muscle	**14** Vertebral artery	## RADIOGRAPHIC KEY
6 Anterior scalene muscle	**15** Levator scapulae muscle	
7 Medial scalene muscle	**16** Longissimus capitis muscle	**a** Tongue
8 Posterior scalene muscle	**17** Splenius capitis muscle	**b** Mandible
9 Superior extent of the brachial plexus	**18** Semispinalis capitis muscle	**c** Cervical vertebrae followed by the corresponding number
	19 Transversospinalis muscle	**d** Fracture
10 Fifth cervical vertebrae	**20** Semispinalis cervicis muscle	**e** Dens epistrophe

PLATE 6-2 LOWER NUCHAL MUSCULATURE *(Visible Man 1248)*

Corresponding CT. Several muscle masses are merged. Neither the levator scapulae and the scalene muscles nor the erector spinae and the splenius muscles can be differentiated. The vertebral spine appears elongate, a morphology more common for C7 (vertebra prominens), leaving little space for the nuchal ligament. Note the collapsed internal jugular vein.

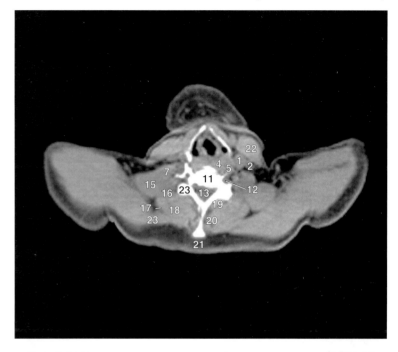

Cryosection. This section passes through the center of the intervertebral disc between the fourth and the fifth cervical vertebrae. Note the fasciculated appearance of levator scapulae at this level as it nears its origin on the transverse processes of C1-4. The grain of the trapezius muscle indicates the horizontal orientation of this portion that inserts inferiorly on the spine of the scapula. Note the midsagittal posterior projection of the ligamentum nuchae, which forms a sheetlike raphe between the large right and left nuchal muscle masses.

Diagnostic Plain-Film Radiograph. Lateral view of the cervical spine shows a fracture through the base of the dens. The lateral view is one of the first views obtained in patients with neck trauma. This view allows rapid initial evaluation of spine alignment for obvious fractures.

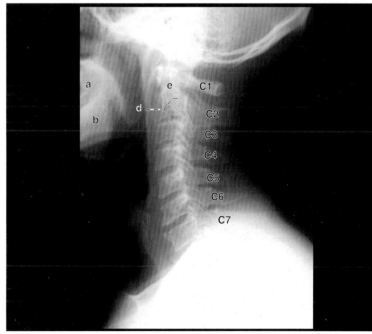

PLATE 6-3 MIDTHORACIC BACK *(Visible Man 1372)*

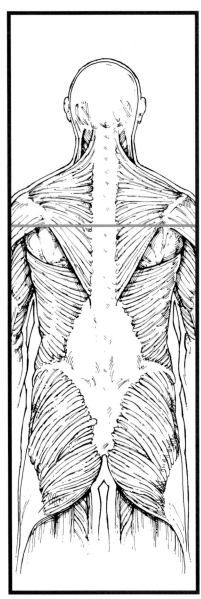

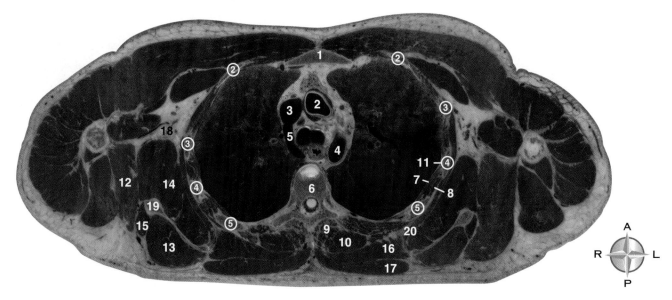

1   Sternum
2   Ascending aorta
3   Superior vena cava
4   Descending aorta
5   Arch of the azygos vein
6   Fifth thoracic vertebra
7   Internal intercostal muscles
8   External intercostal muscles
9   Transversospinalis muscle
10 Spinalis thoracis muscle

11 Rib (corresponding rib numbers are within circles)
12 Latissimus dorsi muscle
13 Infraspinatus muscle
14 Subscapularis muscle
15 Teres minor muscle
16 Rhomboid major muscle
17 Trapezius muscle
18 Brachial plexus
19 Scapula
20 Serratus anterior muscle

RADIOGRAPHIC KEY

a   Intervertebral disc
b   Spinal cord
T   Thoracic vertebrae followed by the corresponding number
S   Spinous process of the thoracic vertebrae followed by the corresponding number

PLATE 6-3 MIDTHORACIC BACK *(Visible Man 1372)*

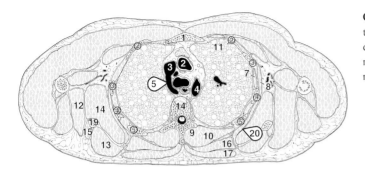

Cryosection. This section passes through thoracic vertebral level 5 (same image as plate 3 of Chapter 2, The Thorax). This level is in the middle portion of the back, as there are no more cervical insertions and none of the muscles have direct pelvic origins. The rib cage is somewhat inflexible so, in humans, the erector spinae has some control over rib cage volume or stabilization. More important, the stable rib cage can act as a mooring for the more mobile scapula. At this level the rhomboid major and serratus anterior muscles are the primary connections between the vertebral column and the scapula.

Corresponding CT. None of the deep back musculature can be differentiated However, the rhomboid major, trapezius, and serratus anterior muscles are clearly defined.

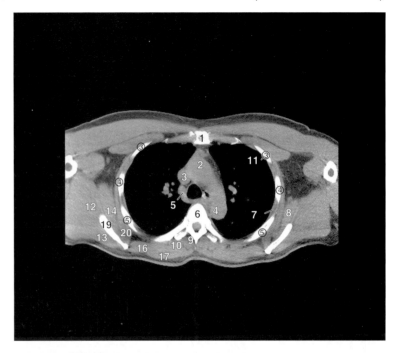

Diagnostic MR. This MR study shows the mid-thoracic spine in lateral view. Note the compression fracture of T5 with bone fragments projecting posteriorly and compressing the spinal cord. Compression fractures often are due to osteoporosis or metastatic tumor. (Key: S, superior; P, posterior; I, inferior; A, anterior.)

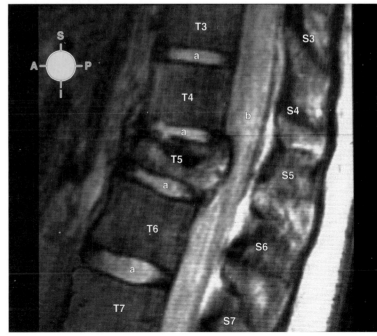

PLATE 6-4 LOWER THORACIC BACK *(Visible Man 1430)*

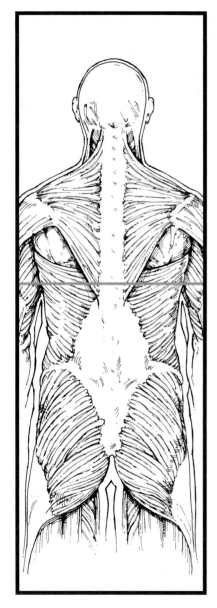

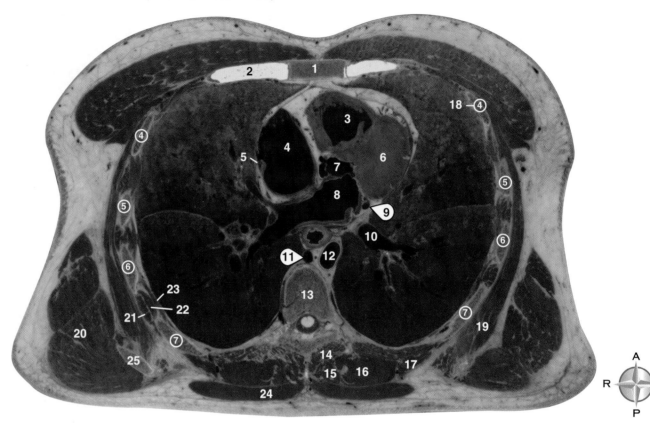

1 Sternum	**12** Descending aorta	**21** External intercostal muscle
2 Costal cartilage	**13** Eighth thoracic vertebra	**22** Internal intercostal muscle
3 Right ventricle	**14** Transversospinalas muscle	**23** Innermost intercostal muscle
4 Right atrium	**15** Spinalis thoracis muscle	**24** Trapezius muscle
5 Right auricle	**16** Longissimus thoracis muscle	**25** Scapula
6 Left ventricle	**17** Iliocostalis muscle	
7 Ascending aorta	**18** Rib (corresponding rib numbers	## RADIOGRAPHIC KEY
8 Left atrium	are within circles)	
9 Left coronary artery	**19** Serratus anterior muscle	**a** Diaphragm
10 Left pulmonary vein	**20** Latissimus dorsi muscle	**T** Thoracic vertebrae followed by
11 Azygous vein		the corresponding number

PLATE 6-4 LOWER THORACIC BACK *(Visible Man 1430)*

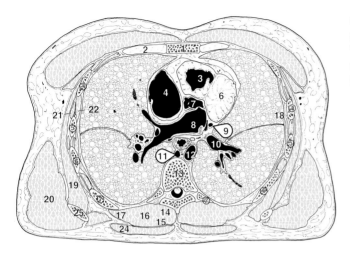

Cryosection. This section passes through the eighth thoracic vertebra. Several muscular components of the erector spinae are independently visible. The inferiormost scapula is visible.

Corresponding CT. None of intrinsic back musculature is visible. The mobile scapula was held superior to this section when this CT scan was taken.

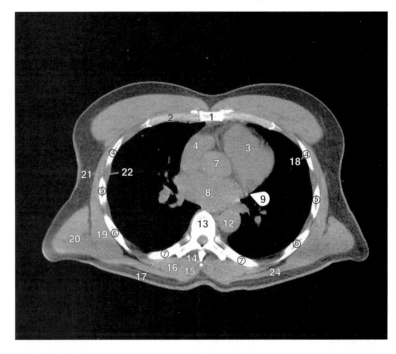

Diagnostic Image. Anterior-to-posterior plain-film thoracic radiograph in a patient following trauma. The spine has been severed between thoracic vertebra T7 and T8 with left lateral dislocation of the superior segment. If stabilized, this individual can be expected to have lower extremity paraplegia and incontinence. (Key: S, superior; L, left; I, inferior; R, right.)

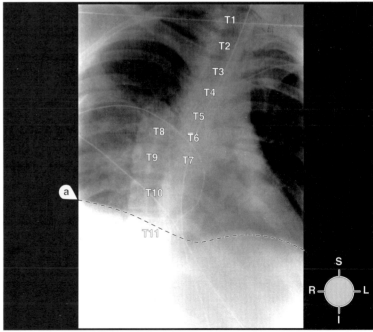

125

PLATE 6-5 MIDLUMBAR BACK *(Visible Man 1715)*

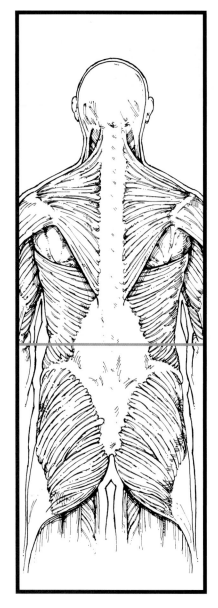

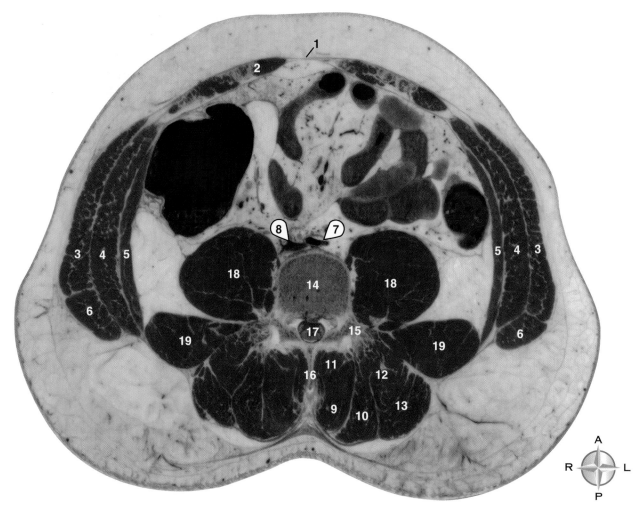

1	Linea alba	10 Longissimus muscle
2	Rectus abdominis muscle	11 Multifidus muscle
3	External oblique muscle	12 Rotatores muscle
4	Internal oblique muscle	13 Iliocostalis muscle
5	Transversus abdominis muscle	14 Fourth lumbar vertebra
6	Latissimus dorsi muscle	15 Transverse process of the lumbar vertebra
7	Descending aorta	16 Spinous process of the lumbar vertebra
8	Inferior vena cava	
9	Spinalis muscle	

17 Cauda equina
18 Psoas major muscle
19 Quadratus lumborum muscle

RADIOGRAPHIC KEY

a Iliac blade
b Erector spinae muscle
c Fracture
d Gluteus medius muscle

PLATE 6-5 MIDLUMBAR BACK *(Visible Man 1715)*

Corresponding CT. As in the cryosection, the L3 horizontal level does not show the kidneys or the iliac crests. Much of the intrinsic back musculature and the oblique muscles are discernible on this CT image.

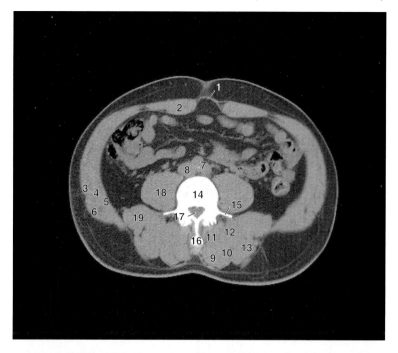

Cryosection. This section passes through the third lumbar vertebra, which falls inbetween the kidneys and the iliac crests. Thus, at this level, L3 is the only bony portion of the abdominal wall. There is also increased risk of intervertebral disc herniation. The left side of the erector spinae (intermediate intrinsic back muscle layer) is labelled. The two visible muscles of the deep intrinsic back muscle layer are also highlighted by the artist.

Diagnostic CT. This section passes through L4. Note that neither the quadratus lumborum nor the latissmus dorsi muscle is present. The former abdominal muscle arises from the iliac crest. The latter back muscle arises from the thoracodorsal aponeurosis, which, in turn, arises from the iliac crest. A blunt trauma has occurred as evidenced by the break of the left iliac blade. Note the concomitant displacement and the probable blood accumulation in the psoas major and the gluteus medius muscles.

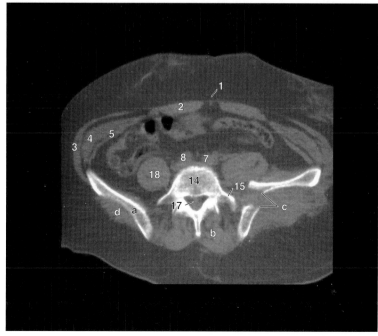

PLATE 6-6 MIDSACRAL BACK *(Visible Man 1805)*

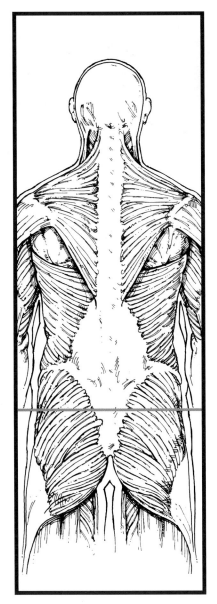

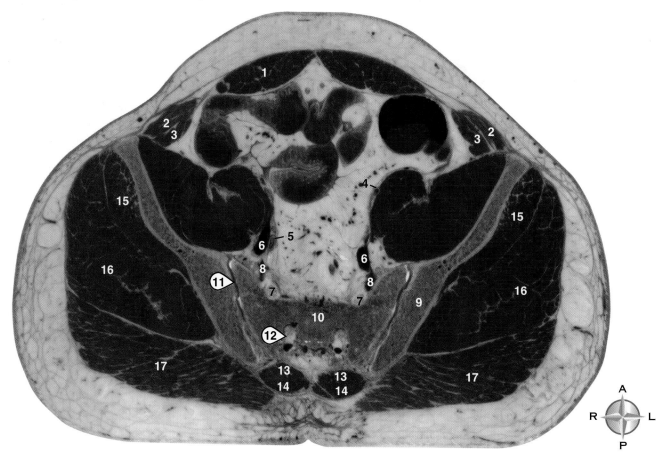

1 Rectus abdominis muscle	**10** Second sacral vertebra	
2 External oblique muscle	**11** Iliosacral joint	
3 Internal oblique muscle	**12** Sacral nerve roots	
4 External iliac artery	**13** Multifidus muscle	
5 Internal iliac artery	**14** Basal erector spinae muscle	
6 Internal iliac vein	**15** Gluteus minimis muscle	
7 Ventral rami	**16** Gluteus medius muscle	
8 Superior gluteal vessels	**17** Gluteus maximus muscle	
9 Iliac blade of the pelvis		

RADIOGRAPHIC KEY

a Sacral promontory
b Arcuate line
C Coccygeal vertebrae followed by the corresponding number
d Linea terminalis
e Pecten pubis
f Ischial spine
L Lumbar vertebrae followed by the corresponding number

PLATE 6-6 MIDSACRAL BACK *(Visible Man 1805)*

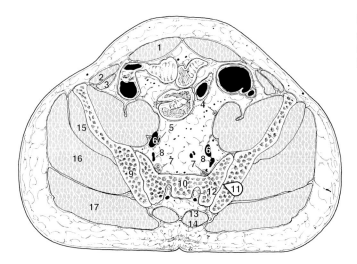

Cryosection. This section passes through the transverse processes of the second sacral vertebra, which contribute to the iliosacral joint just below the division of the internal and the external iliac vessels. This is the inferiormost extent of the erector spinae (intermediate intrinsic) and multifidus (deep intrinsic) muscles of the back. Note the merger of the iliacus and psoas into the iliopsoas muscle, which is an important ventral flexing antagonist of the erector spinae and the gluteus maximus muscles' dorsiflexion of the trunk.

Corresponding CT. Axial CT section through S1 highlights the muscular and the bony structures seen in the cryosection.

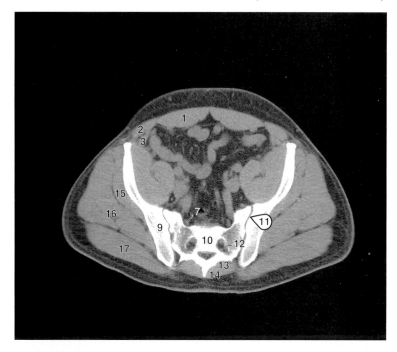

Corresponding MR. Obese males and females may develop lower back problems caused by weight-induced strain driving L5 anteriorly off the sacrum—a process known as lumbar march. Like much of the female pelvic anatomy, dimensions tend to be relatively wider than in males. Thus the sacral promontory and the lower sacral segments tend to be anteroposteriorly flattened and mediolaterally wide. These proportions make for a somewhat larger pelvic inlet circumference. The female sacral and the coccygeal vertebrae, as well as the ischial spines, tend to be short and vertically arrayed inferosuperiorly. All of these proportions reduce the medial projection of structures supporting the pelvic floor into the birth canal.

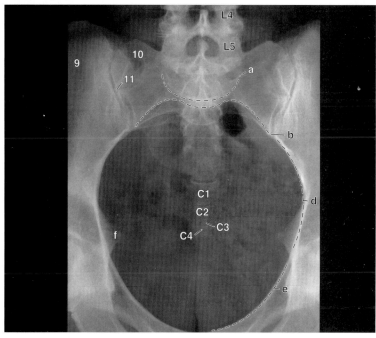

CHAPTER 7

Upper Limb

INTRODUCTION

The upper limb is frequently injured during falls onto an outstretched arm. Impact force on a fully extended upper extremity tends to run cranially through the scaphoid (a proximal row carpal bone), radius, humerus, and clavicle. The most common fracture points are the scaphoid, radial head, and midclavicular (anterior) arc. Plain-film radiographs are the most common diagnostic images taken of these fractures; however, one needs to be cognizant of epiphyseal sites in the young that may mimic fractures or become dislocated. More complex injuries to joints, ligaments, and muscles are often better seen with magnetic resonance (MR) imaging. In the shoulder, the rotator cuff and glenohumeral joint bursa are common sites of injury. In the arm (brachium), the large flexors, especially biceps brachii, are commonly injured. In the elbow, forearm, and wrist, muscles are often strained. Chronic fatigue injuries of the shoulder, elbow, and wrist are common. Carpal tunnel syndrome is common among typists who undergo repeated strain of the forearm (antebrachium) muscle tendons passing under the flexor retinaculum and through the carpal tunnel (Fig. 7-1).

The first section passes through the upper shoulder, including the glenohumeral joint (the Visible Human cryosection image here is equivalent to that seen in Chapter 9, Plate 9-4). Beginning with Plate 7-2, all cross sections are of the left side. Plates 7-2 and 7-3 are of the middle and the distal brachium (anatomical arm). Plates 7-4, 7-5,

FIGURE 7-1 Serial Relation of Flexor and Extensor Compartments. Anterior flexor and posterior extensor muscular compartments are in the arm and forearm. Note that proximally, the common forearm extensor origin is found laterally and the common forearm flexor origin is found medially. The two intrinsic hand muscle compartments of the hand, thenar (lateral compartment) and hypothenar (medial compartment), primarily contain thumb and finger muscles of abduction, flexion, and opposition. The muscle bodies of their counterparts are primarily located in the forearm. Therefore, as with the middle compartment of the hand, only the long tendons of these muscles are seen in the wrist and hand. Key: Plate 7-2: (1) brachium (arm) flexor muscles, (2) brachium (arm) extensor muscles; Plate 7-3: (3) brachium (arm) flexor muscles passing over the elbow, (4) brachium (arm) extensor muscles passing over the elbow; Plate 7-4: (5) antebrachium (forearm) flexor muscles, (6) antebrachium (forearm) extensor muscles; Plate 7-8: (7) antebrachium (forearm) digital flexor tendons, (8) antebrachium (forearm) digital extensor tendons (middle compartment), (9) thenar (first digit) muscles (lateral compartment), (10) hypothenar (fifth digit) muscles (medial compartment).

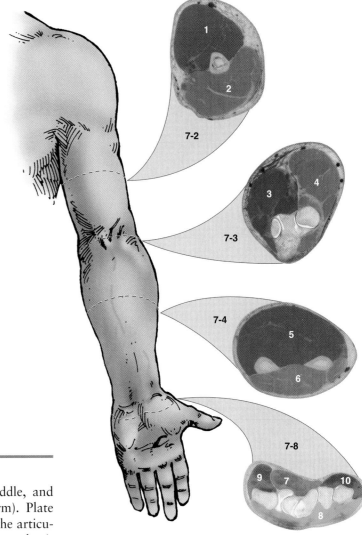

and 7-6 are through the proximal, middle, and distal antebrachium (anatomical forearm). Plate 7-6 shows the wrist. Plate 7-8 presents the articulation between the carpus and the metacarpal origin of the digits (rays). Notes are made where the cryosection images of the Visible Man are inconsistent with what would be seen were he in anatomical position. From the elbow distally his arms are medially rotated.

PLATE 7-1 PROXIMAL HUMERUS AND SHOULDER *(Visible Man 1321)*

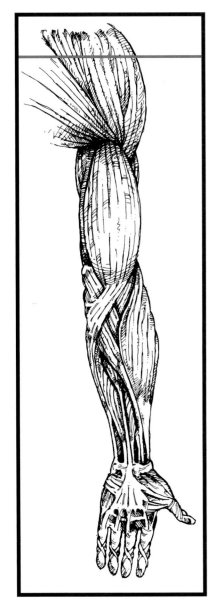

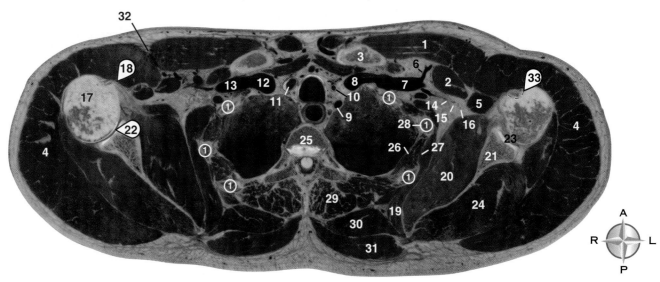

1	Pectoralis major muscle	16 Axillary nerve	29 Erector spinae
2	Pectoralis minor muscle	17 Humerus	30 Rhomboid major muscle
3	Clavicle	18 Long tendon of the biceps muscle	31 Trapezius muscle
4	Deltoid muscle	19 Serratus anterior muscle	32 Cephalic vein
5	Coracobrachialis muscle	20 Subscapularis muscle	33 Bicipital groove of the humerus

1 Pectoralis major muscle
2 Pectoralis minor muscle
3 Clavicle
4 Deltoid muscle
5 Coracobrachialis muscle
6 Left thoracoacromial vein
7 Left subclavian vein
8 Left brachiocephalic vein
9 Left subclavian artery
10 Left common carotid artery
11 Brachiocephalic artery
12 Right brachiocephalic vein
13 Right subclavian vein
14 Ulnar nerve
15 Radial nerve

16 Axillary nerve
17 Humerus
18 Long tendon of the biceps muscle
19 Serratus anterior muscle
20 Subscapularis muscle
21 Scapula
22 Glenoid fossa
23 Glenohumeral joint
24 Infraspinatus muscle
25 First thoracic vertebra with intervertebral disc
26 Internal intercostal muscle
27 External intercostal muscle
28 Rib (corresponding rib numbers are within circles)

29 Erector spinae
30 Rhomboid major muscle
31 Trapezius muscle
32 Cephalic vein
33 Bicipital groove of the humerus

RADIOGRAPHIC KEY

a Coracoid process of the scapula
b Greater tubercle
c Head
d Surgical neck
e Labrum
f Acromion
g Acromioclavicular joint
h Rotator cuff

132

PLATE 7-1 PROXIMAL HUMERUS AND SHOULDER *(Visible Man 1321)*

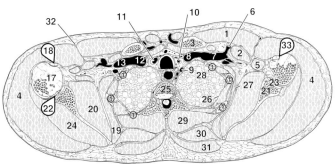

Cryosection. This section is at the level of the second thoracic vertebra just inferior to the apex of the shoulders and passes inferior to the scapular spine and notch as evidenced by the view of the subscapularis and the infraspinatus muscles, two of the four muscles (i.e., subscapularis, infraspinatus, teres minor, and supraspinatus, forming the mnemonic SITS) inserting into the rotator cuff. Note the presence of the three portions of the deltoid muscle surrounding the humeral head. The bicipital groove in the humeral head is present on both sides; however, the infraspinatus muscle insertion is only visible from the right side. Note that the base of the scapular glenoid fossa is well visualized, whereas a good view of the superior humeral joint surface requires elevation of the arms. Also appreciate how the pectoralis minor and the coracobrachialis muscles insert on opposing sides of the coracoid process. Last, note the limitation on scapular movement, and the arm as well, imposed by contraction of the serratus anterior, rhomboid major, and trapezius muscles, all visible on this plate.

Corresponding CT. Same axial section as seen in the cryosection. Note the muscular tonus raising the body ventrally from medial to lateral in this image lateral. Similarly, the skin is more firmly attached to the vertebral spines and scapular muscles than in the Visible Man image. The jugular notch between the two clavicular heads is seen as a space with the manubrium found inferiorly. This image clearly presents the bed of muscles in which the scapula is seated. For this reason the strain borne by one's weight landing on the upper extremity is transmitted to the clavicular head abutting the manubrium.

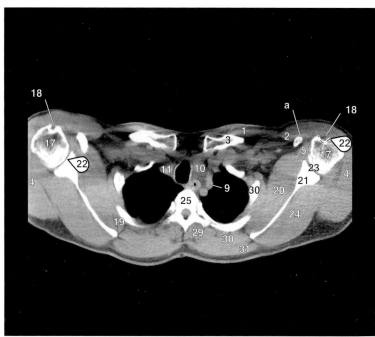

Diagnostic Image. Oblique MR section through the right shoulder. The orientation image at the lower left is an axial view in the region where the shoulder MR coil was placed. The white line shows the orientation of the larger image. It is an oblique coronal view halfway between true sagittal and true coronal. This view shows the wide variety and range of motion available to the humeral head (circumduction, rotation, flexion, extension, abduction, adduction, elevation, and depression). Note the small portion of the humeral head, roughly a third, that can oppose the glenoid fossa at any one time. The acromion process and clavicle bound it superiorly. In addition to these two bony braces, the rotator cuff tendon sheath and the tendon for the long head of the biceps muscle provide stability to this joint.

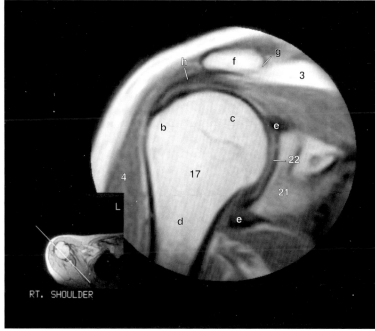

RT. SHOULDER

133

PLATE 7-2 MID-DIAPHYSIS LEFT HUMERUS *(Visible Man 1480)*

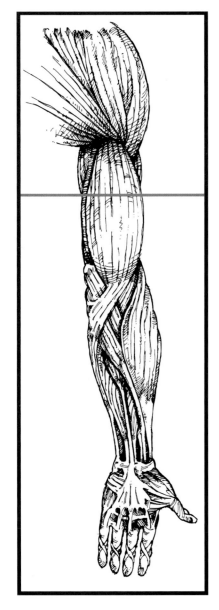

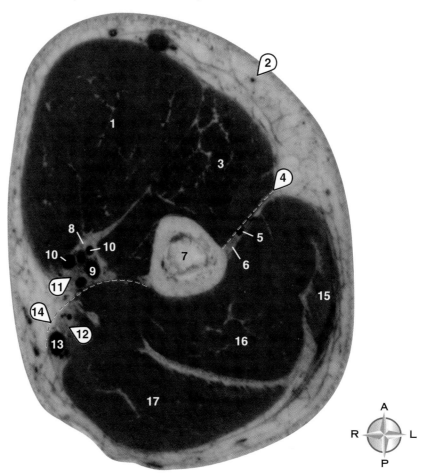

1	Biceps muscle	12	Ulnar nerve	d	Medial epicondyle
2	Cephalic vein	13	Basilic vein	e	Lateral epicondyle
3	Brachialis muscle	14	Medial intermuscular septum	f	Capitulum
4	Lateral intermuscular septum	15	Lateral head of the triceps muscle	g	Trochlea
5	Profunda brachii artery	16	Medial head of the triceps muscle	h	Radius bone
6	Radial nerve	17	Long head of the triceps muscle	i	Head of the radius
7	Humerus			j	Neck of the radius
8	Musculocutaneous nerve			k	Radial tuberosity
9	Brachial artery	**RADIOGRAPHIC KEY**		l	Ulna bone
10	Venae comitantes of the brachial artery	a	Cortex of the humerus bone	m	Coronoid process
		b	Marrow cavity of the humerus bone	n	Proximal radioulnar joint
11	Median nerve	c	Olecranon process		

134

PLATE 7-2 MID-DIAPHYSIS LEFT HUMERUS *(Visible Man 1480)*

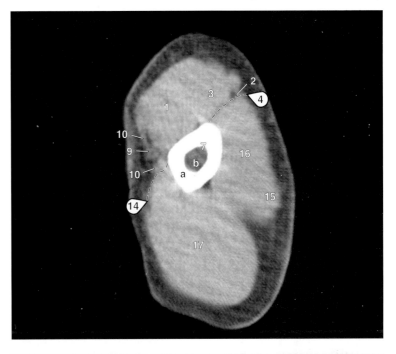

Corresponding CT. This section of a live person is through a level of the anatomical arm (L. brachium) that is homologous to that seen in the cryosection image. The marrow cavity of the humerus is well visualized. The tonus of the biceps and triceps muscles give the anterior and the posterior compartments nearly reversed shapes between these two images.

Cryosection. This section divides the upper and the middle halves of the humeral shaft. There is a tight sleeve of outer investing fascia to the muscles in the arm, which assists muscular contractions to force blood back to the heart more efficiently. The anterior (ventral) flexor and posterior (dorsal) extensor compartments are divided by the medial and the lateral intermuscular septa. The ulnar nerve, artery (branch of the brachial artery), and vein pass through the medial intermuscular septum distally. The radial nerve, profunda brachii artery, and profunda brachii vein wrap around the humerus posteriorly more distally passing through the lateral intermuscular septum. These three structures are visible posteriorly through the triangular interval formed by the teres major muscle superiorly and the medial and the long head of the triceps muscle. The brachial plexus is particularly vulnerable at this level, especially during and after fracture, dislocation, or both the adult humeral head or unfused proximal epiphysis of children.

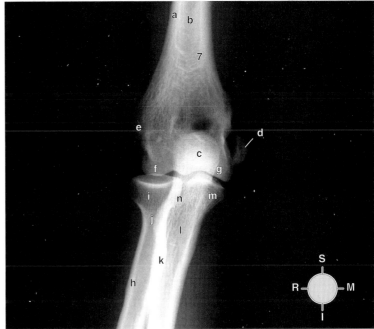

Diagnostic Image. Posterior-to-anterior view of an adult right elbow. Note that the olecranon process and fossa, both behind the humerus, is less clearly visible than the anterior structures closer to the film. The medial epicondyle appears to be fractured, possibly causing problems with the associated ulnar nerve. (Key: S, superior; M, medial; I, inferior; R, right.)

PLATE 7-3 LEFT ELBOW *(Visible Man 1602)*

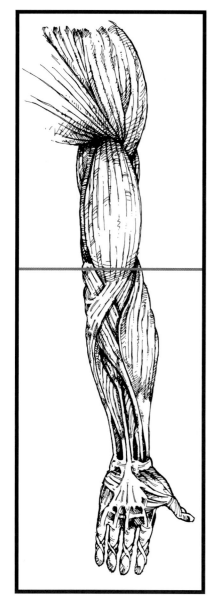

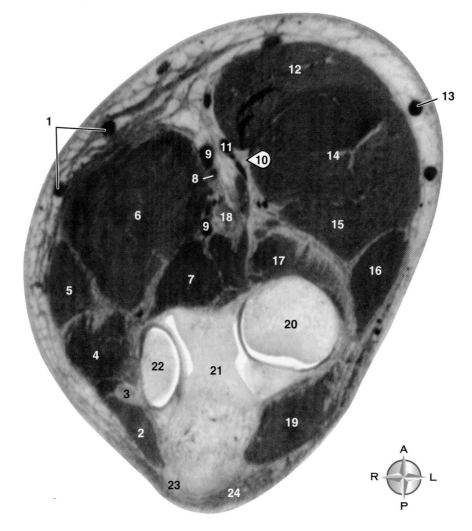

1   Basilic vein
2   Flexor carpi ulnaris muscle
3   Ulnar nerve
4   Flexor digitorum superficialis muscle
5   Flexor carpi radialis muscle
6   Common flexor muscle origin
7   Brachialis muscle
8   Brachial artery

9   Venae comitantes of the brachial artery
10 Radial nerve
11 Radial recurrent artery
12 Brachioradialis muscle
13 Cephalic vein
14 Extensor carpi radialis longus muscle
15 Extensor carpi radialis brevis muscle

16 Common extensor muscle origin
17 Supinator muscle
18 Biceps muscle tendon
19 Anconeus muscle
20 Radius
21 Ulna
22 Trochlea of the humerus
23 Triceps muscle tendon insertion
24 Olecranon bursa

PLATE 7-4 PROXIMAL LEFT ANTEBRACHIUM *(Visible Man 1663)*

Corresponding CT. Section taken in anatomical position, however, the flexor compartment was deflected somewhat medially. The subject was lying prone for this scan. The bones and both the flexor and extensor muscle compartments are clearly visualized.

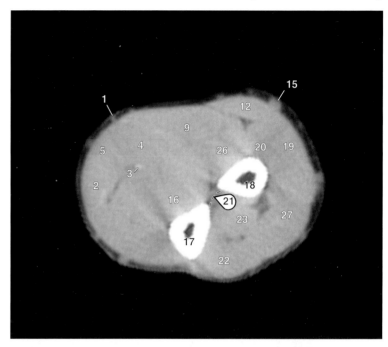

Cryosection. This section passes through the proximal antebrachium, between the elbow and the wrist, approximately between the proximal and the middle thirds of the forearm. Note that the obliquity of the forearm makes this section mediolaterally elongate, whereas in anatomical position dorsoventral would be the greatest dimension. Note the supinator muscle wrapping around the radius.

Corresponding MR. This section was taken in anatomical position and thus no portion is deflected or compressed. Cortical bone and vessels are low in signal. Note that the forearm (antebrachium) shaft has much less subcutaneous fat than the anatomical, or upper, arm (brachium).

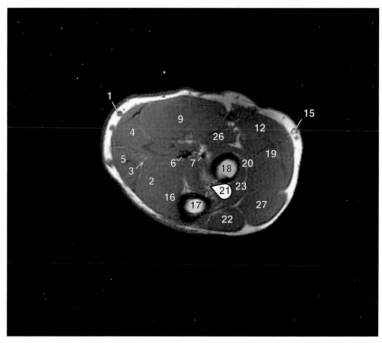

PLATE 7-5 MID-LEFT ANTEBRACHIUM *(Visible Man 1700)*

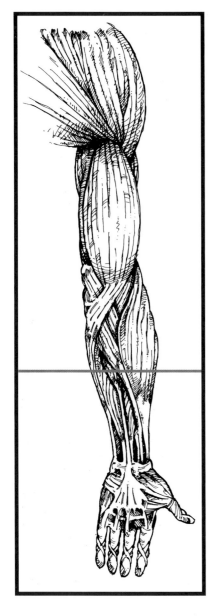

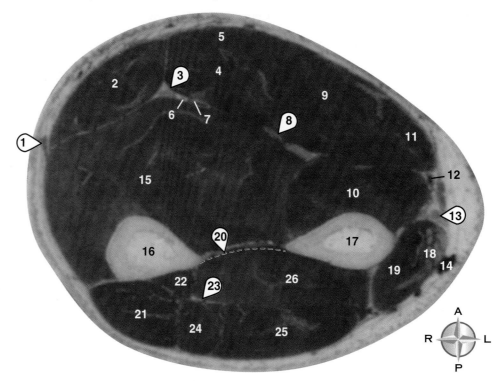

1 Basilic vein	10 Flexor pollicis longus muscle	19 Extensor carpi radialis brevis muscle tendon
2 Flexor carpi ulnaris muscle	11 Brachioradialis muscle tendon	20 Interosseous membrane
3 Ulnar nerve	12 Radial artery	21 Extensor carpi ulnaris muscle
4 Flexor digitorum superficialis muscle	13 Radial nerve	22 Extensor pollicis longus muscle
5 Palmaris longus muscle tendon	14 Cephalic vein	23 Posterior interosseous vessels and nerve
6 Ulnar vein	15 Flexor digitorum profundus muscle	24 Extensor digiti minimi muscle
7 Ulnar artery	16 Ulna	25 Extensor digitorum muscle
8 Median nerve	17 Radius	26 Abductor pollicis longus muscle
9 Flexor carpi radialis muscle and tendon	18 Extensor carpi radialis longus muscle tendon	

PLATE 7-5 MID-LEFT ANTEBRACHIUM *(Visible Man 1700)*

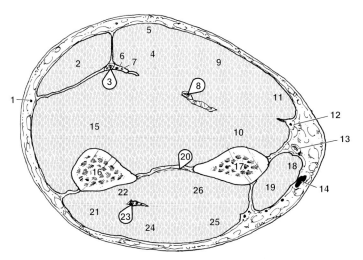

Corresponding CT. Flexor and extensor muscle compartments are clearly visualized. The proportions of structures are similar to those seen in the Visible Man image.

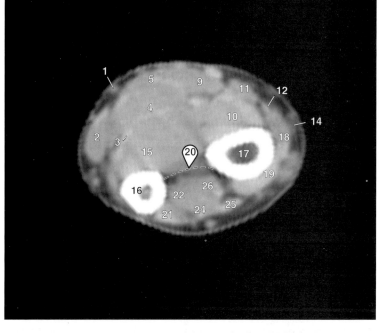

Cryosection. This section passes through the midantebrachium, halfway between the elbow and the wrist. There appears to be reduced mediolaterally elongation owing to the oblique orientation of the Visible Man antebrachium. Otherwise, the proportions of the visible structures appear similar to those held in the anatomical position in the corresponding CT and MR images. Note the distinct attachment sites and position of the interosseous membrane separating the flexor and the extensor muscle compartments.

Corresponding MR. Compact bone and veins are dark. The orientation of the flexor and extensor compartment muscles is similar to the cryosection and corresponding CT views. The proportional sizes and orientation of muscles in these compartments change substantially as the orientation of the patient to the scan plane changes.

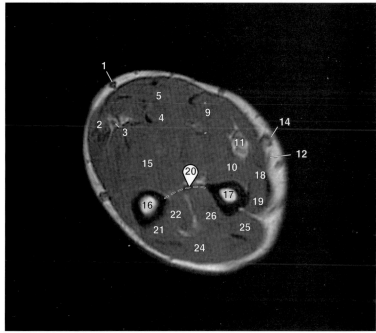

PLATE 7-6 **DISTALMOST LEFT ANTEBRACHIUM** *(Visible Man 1758)*

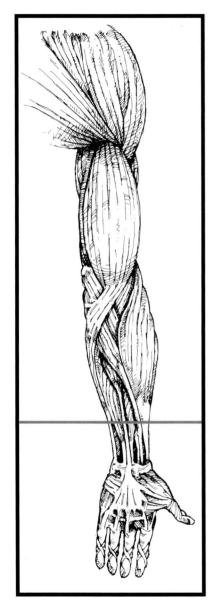

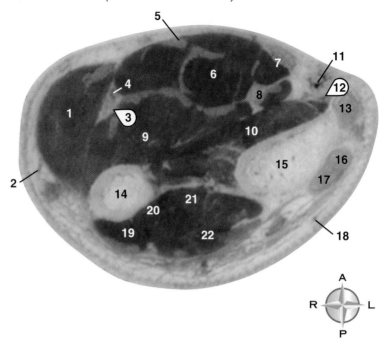

1 Flexor carpi ulnaris muscle	8 Median nerve	16 Extensor carpi radialis longus muscle tendon
2 Basilic vein	9 Flexor digitorum profundus muscle	17 Extensor carpi radialis brevis muscle tendon
3 Ulnar nerve	10 Flexor pollicis longus muscle	18 Cephalic vein
4 Ulnar artery	11 Radial artery	19 Extensor carpi ulnaris muscle
5 Palmaris longus muscle tendon	12 Radial nerve	20 Extensor pollicis longus muscle
6 Flexor digitorum superficialis muscle	13 Brachioradialis muscle tendon	21 Abductor pollicis longus muscle
7 Flexor carpi radialis muscle and tendon	14 Ulna	22 Extensor digitorum muscle
	15 Radius	

PLATE 7-6 DISTALMOST LEFT ANTEBRACHIUM (*Visible Man 1758*)

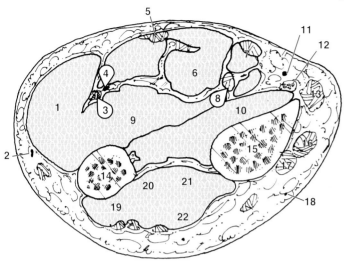

Corresponding CT. The Visible Man apparently has more muscular wrists than the patient imaged here. This section is also slightly more distal than either the cryosection or the corresponding MR image. The size of these muscles varies between individuals, between sexes, and with age. The sharp lateral prominence of the radius suggests a slightly more distal radial styloid process in the CT image.

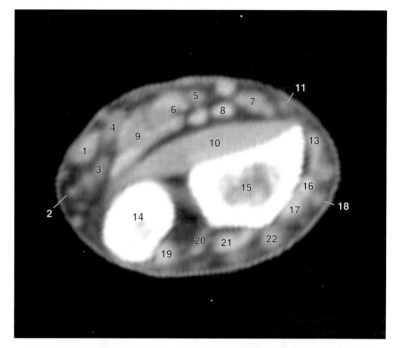

Cryosection. This section passes through the distalmost antebrachium, just proximal to the wrist. There appears to be little elongation owing to the oblique orientation (i.e., not in anatomical position) of the Visible Man antebrachium and hand. The interosseous membrane clearly separates the flexor and extensor muscle compartments.

Corresponding MR. Compact bone and veins appear dark. There appears to be significantly more subcutaneous fat dorsally (posterior) than ventrally (anterior).

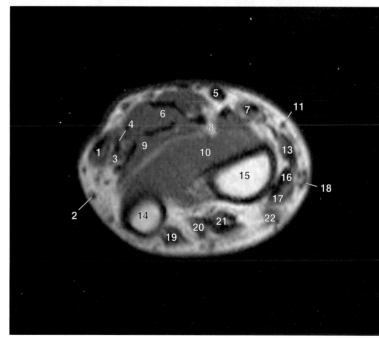

PLATE 7-7 LEFT MIDCARPAL JOINTS *(Visible Man 1772)*

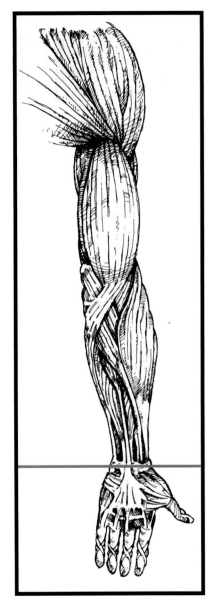

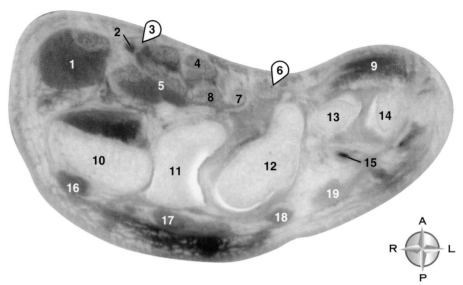

1   Muscles of the hypothenar
    eminence
2   Ulnar artery
3   Ulnar nerve
4   Palmaris longus muscle tendon
5   Flexor digitorum profundus
    muscle tendon
6   Median nerve
7   Flexor pollicis longus muscle
    tendon
8   Flexor carpi radialis muscle
    tendon
9   Muscles of the thenar eminence
10 Triquetrum
11 Hamate

12 Capitate
13 Trapezoid
14 Trapezium
15 Radial artery
16 Extensor carpi ulnaris muscle
    tendon
17 Extensor digitorum muscle tendon
18 Extensor carpi radialis longus
    muscle tendon
19 Extensor pollicis longus muscle
    tendon

RADIOGRAPHIC KEY

a   Hook of the hamate
b   Radius

c   Styloid process of the radius
d   Ulna
e   Styloid process of the ulna
f   Scaphoid
g   Fracture
h   Trapezium
i   Tubercle of the trapezium
j   Trapezoid
k   Capitate
l   Hamate
M   Metacarpals followed by the
    corresponding number
n   Lunate
o   Pisiform

PLATE 7-7 LEFT MIDCARPAL JOINTS *(Visible Man 1772)*

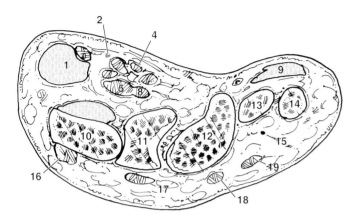

Cryosection. An oblique section that passes through the carpal region that is more proximal on the right (ulnar or medially) than on the left (radially or laterally). This is why the hypothenar eminence appears larger than the thenar eminence.

Corresponding CT. Section taken in anatomical position through the proximal (first) carpal row. This image highlights the proximal attachments of the flexor retinaculum. Medially (ulnar), it is the pisiform. Laterally (radial), it is the scaphoid tubercle. There may be distension of the carpal tunnel and compression of the median nerve in carpal tunnel syndrome.

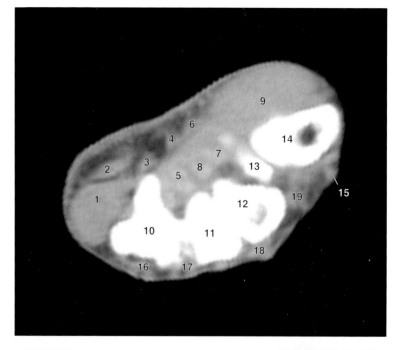

Diagnostic Plain Film Radiograph. A wrist plain-film x-ray shows a comminuted (several fragments) fracture of the distal radius. Note the relationship of the bones in the carpus. Note the orientation of the scaphoid and compare it to Plate 7-8.

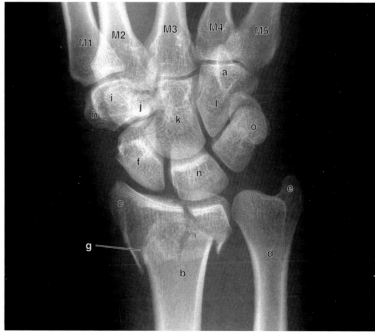

PLATE 7-8 LEFT CARPOMETACARPAL JOINTS *(Visible Man 1776)*

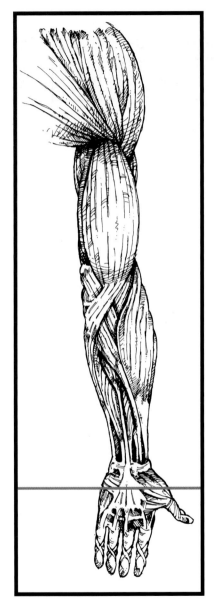

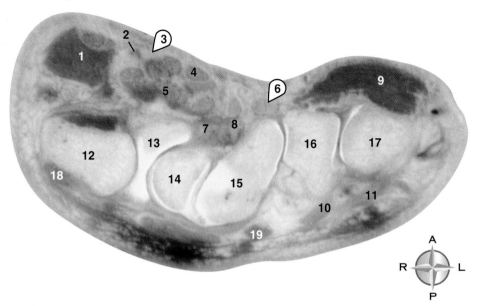

1	Muscles of the hypothenar eminence	11	Extensor pollicis brevis muscle tendon
2	Ulnar artery	12	Triquetrum
3	Ulnar nerve	13	Hamate
4	Palmaris longus muscle tendon	14	Capitate
5	Flexor digitorum profundus muscle tendon	15	Trapezoid
6	Median nerve	16	Trapezium
7	Flexor pollicis longus muscle tendon	17	First metacarpal
8	Flexor carpi radialis muscle tendon	18	Extensor carpi ulnaris muscle tendon
9	Muscles of the thenar eminence	19	Extensor carpi radialis muscle tendon
10	Abductor pollicis longus muscle tendon		

RADIOGRAPHIC KEY

a Hook of the hamate
b Radius
c Styloid process of the radius
d Ulna
e Styloid process of the ulna
f Distal radioulnar joint
g Scaphoid
h Fracture
i Trapezium
j Tubercle of the trapezium
k Trapezoid
l Capitate
M Metacarpals followed by the corresponding number
n Hamate
o Lunate
p Pisiform

PLATE 7-8 LEFT CARPOMETACARPAL JOINTS *(Visible Man 1776)*

Corresponding CT.   Section taken in anatomical position through the distal (second) carpal row. It highlights the proximal attachments of the flexor retinaculum. Medially (ulnar), it is the hook of the hamate. Laterally (radial), it is the tubercle of the trapezium. There may be distension of the carpal tunnel and compression of the median nerve in carpal tunnel syndrome.

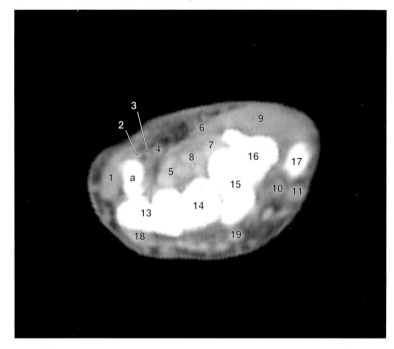

Cryosection.   An oblique section that passes through the carpometacarpal region. It is more proximal on the right (ulnar or medially) than on the left (radially or laterally). The articulation between the base of the first metacarpal and the trapezium is seen.

Diagnostic Plain-film Radiograph.   Anterior-to-posterior coronal (frontal) plain-film radiograph of an adult's left hand. There is a scaphoid fracture. This is a common result of a hard fall onto an outstretched hand. Pain is felt there from pressure applied to the anatomical snuff box. Note the orientation of the scaphoid compared to Plate 7-7. Scaphoid fractures can be difficult to diagnose by x-ray, often requiring multiple views.

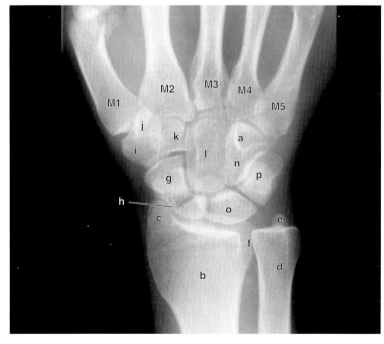

147

CHAPTER 8

Head

INTRODUCTION

The head contains many small structures packed into a roughly spherical region of 9 to 10 in. (23 to 25 cm) diameter. The most complex of these structures is the brain (cerebrum and cerebellum), which is little discussed in most gross anatomy curricula. Two fluid-filled structures, the cerebral ventricles and the venous sinuses, that articulate with and surround the brain are a common topic of gross anatomy curricula. The three-dimensional (3D) structure of the cerebral ventricles is shown in Figure 8-1. The cerebrospinal fluid (CSF) produced in this space normally drains into the subarachnoid space via the foraminae of Luschka (lateral) (9) and Magendie (median) (10) of the fourth ventricle (8). A wide variety of causes of stenosis (e.g., congenital malformation, tumor, aneurysm) anywhere in or near the cerebral ventricles may lead to high-pressure hydrocephalus (water on the brain). The diagnostic image in Plate 8-2 presents a lateral view of subdural venous sinus drainage.

The blood supply of the brain derives primarily from the internal carotid and vertebral arteries. The vertebral arteries enter the cranial vault at the foramen magnum and merge on the basioccipital or sphenoid clivus into the basilar artery. The posterior inferior cerebellar arteries usually branch from the vertebral arteries before the basilar merge; however, the anterior inferior cerebellar and anterior superior cerebellar arteries usually arise from the basilar artery before it passes through the tentorium into the middle cranial fossa ventral to the brainstem. The basilar artery enters the Cerebral Arterial Circle (of Willis) pos-

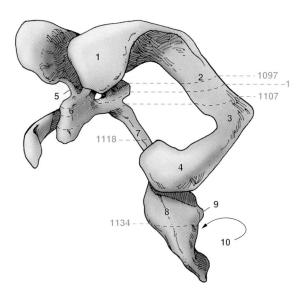

FIGURE 8-1 Cerebral Ventricles. Frontal horn (1), parietal portion (2), occipital horn (3), and temporal horn (4) of the right and the left lateral ventricles drain CSF into the third ventricle (6) via the foramina of Monro (5). The third ventricle drains into the fourth ventricle (8) via the cerebral aqueduct (of Sylvius; 7).

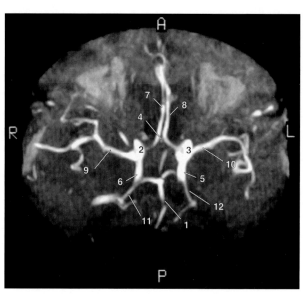

FIGURE 8-2 Cerebral Arterial Circle (of Willis). Major source of the cerebral blood supply. The circle receives three inputs: 1, basilar; 2, right internal carotid; and 3, left internal carotid arteries. The circle has three communicating arteries: one anterior on the 4 and two posterior on the 5 (left) and the 6 (right). There are six cerebral arterial branches: 7, right anterior cerebral; 8, left anterior cerebral; 9, right middle cerebral; 10, left middle cerebral; 11, left posterior cerebral; and 12, right posterior cerebral.

teriorly, whereas the two internal carotid arteries join it laterally after passing through the cavernous sinus. The Cerebral Arterial Circle is rarely in a single axial plane and is not well visualized in the Visible Man data. It is shown as a projection radiographic image in Figure 8-2.

It is common for closely spaced series of tomographic images to be used to study the complex anatomy of organs encircling the cranial base: the orbits, the cavernous sinus region, and the ear. The orbits are presented in Plates 8-1 through 8-5. The right and the left venous cavernous sinuses (Fig. 8-3) are clinically important intradural passageways found on either side of the sphenoid body. The oculomotor nerve (1) enters this space above the petroclinoid ligament (2) whereas the trochlear (3), abdu-

cent (4), and trigeminal (5) nerves all enter below this ligament. All of these nerves pass out of this space anteriorly into orbit through the superior orbital fissure (9). The internal carotid artery emerges from the carotid canal and courses anteriorly through the cavernous sinus but then recurves, with the upper half of its hairpin loop leaving the cavernous sinus under the anterior clinoid process.

The ear is formed by three separate cavities, external, middle, and internal, shown in Figure 8-4. The latter two are seated entirely in the petrous

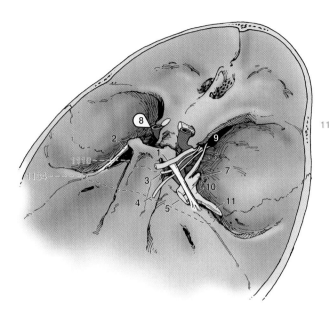

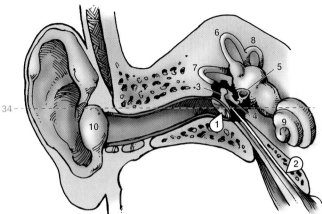

8-4 Ear. Coronal section of the external auditory meatus also includes anatomy of the internal ear that is found anterior to the external ear. Note that the tragus (10) of the auricle, also anterior to the section through the external auditory meatus, is also shown.

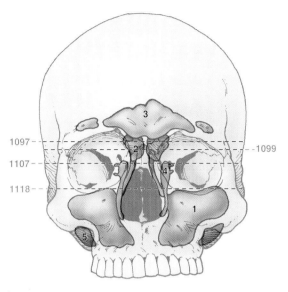

8-5 Paranasal Sinuses. Frontal view of the skull shows the position of all but the sphenoid sinus relative to the nasal cavity in black.

8-3 Cavernous Sinus. Pneumonic o'tomcat is often written thusly:

C
A
OTOM

to indicate that only the internal carotid (8) and the abducent nerve (4) are found suspended in the trabeculae of the cavernous sinus, whereas the oculomotor (1), trochlear (3), ophthalmic (6), and maxillary (7) nerves are all found lodged in the lateral dural wall of this venous sinus. Note that the trigeminal ganglion (10) and the mandibular nerve (11) are found lateral to the cavernous sinus.

temporal bone. The external ear ends at the tympanic membrane (eardrum; 1). The chorda tympani branch of cranial nerve VII runs across its internal surface lateral to the first of three vibrating ossicles. The manubrium of the malleus (3) is lodged in the tympanic membrane. Its vibrations are modulated

by the tensor tympani (2). The malleus has a joint with the incus superiorly in the epitympanic space of the middle ear chamber (shown in black). The incus (4) articulates with the stapes (5). The footplate of the stapes transmits vibration to the oval window (fenestra ovale) of the internal ear chamber. The vestibular apparatus is made up of three orthogonal semicircular canals: anterior (or superior; 6), lateral (or horizontal; 7), and posterior (8). The cochlea (9) is situated anteromedially to the vestibular apparatus within the petrous bone.

The paranasal sinuses, shown in Figure 8-5, enlarge during childhood and adolescence. At birth only the maxillary (1) and ethmoid (2) sinuses are present. The 3-18 ethmoid cells are divided into three groups: anterior, middle, and posterior. The

anterior and the middle cells drain into the hiatus semilunaris with the maxillary sinus. The frontal sinus (3), originally an outgrowth of an anterior ethmoidal cell, develops its own frontonasal duct that may drain either into or just anterior to the hiatus semilunaris. The maxillary sinus also drains into the hiatus semilunaris. The sphenoid sinus is an extension of the posterior ethmoid cell. Both of these cells may drain into the superior meatus or a superoposterior extension of it referred to as the sphenoethmoidal recess. The nasolacrimal duct (tear duct; 4) drains into the inferior meatus. The mastoid air cells (5) also form during adolescence as an outgrowth of the posterior middle-ear cavity by way of the additus ad antrum.

PLATE 8-1 SUPERIORMOST ORBIT (*Visible Man 1097*)

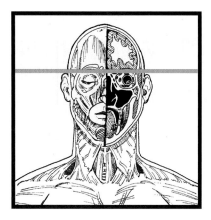

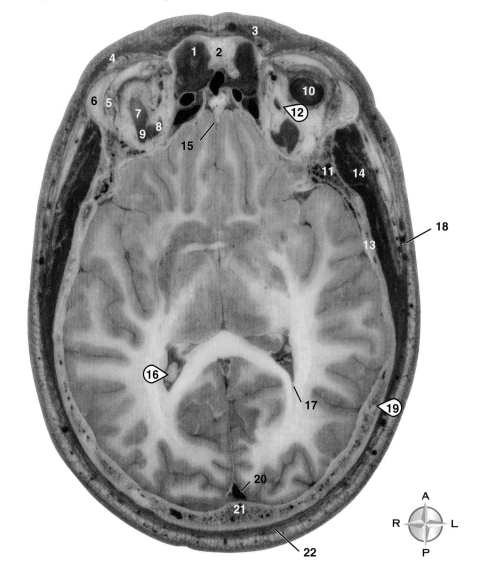

1 Mucosa of the anterior ethmoidal air cell
2 Cribriform plate of the ethmoid bone
3 Frontalis muscle
4 Orbicularis oculi muscle
5 Lacrimal gland
6 Zygomatic process of the frontal bone
7 Levator palpebrae superioris muscle
8 Superior oblique muscle
9 Superior rectus muscle
10 Oculus (eye)
11 Greater wing of the sphenoid bone
12 Ophthalmic artery
13 Squamous portion of the temporal bone
14 Temporalis muscle
15 Crista galli of the ethmoid bone
16 Choroid plexus
17 Posterior horn of the lateral ventricle
18 Superficial temporal vessels
19 Diploe of the parietal bone
20 Superior sagittal sinus
21 Groove for the superior sagittal sinus on the occipital bone

22 Occipital muscle

RADIOGRAPH KEY

a Lateral rectus muscle
b Medial rectus muscle
c Inferior rectus muscle
d Inferior oblique muscle
e Middle meatus
f Inferior meatus
g Maxillary sinus
h Infundibulum
i Maxilla bone
j Perpendicular plate of the ethmoid bone

k Anterior nasal spine
l Incisor
m Canine
n Zygomatic bone
o Optic nerve
p Frontal bone
q Sphenoethmoidal recess

PLATE 8-1 SUPERIORMOST ORBIT *(Visible Man 1097)*

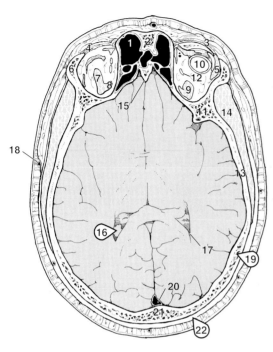

Corresponding CT. Position of the superior sagittal sinus is not as clear on this image. The low radiodensity of the orbital fat gives the orbital bone greater clarity. Unlike the cryosection, posteriorly the two parietal portions of the cerebral ventricle are nearly approximated.

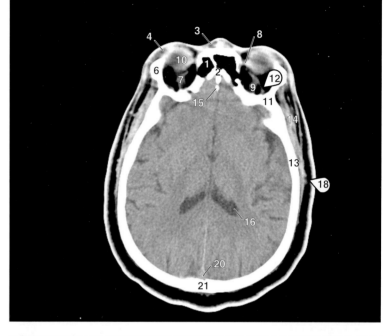

Cryosection. Just below the scalp, anteriorly, there appear to be fibers of the frontalis and possibly corrugator muscles. The frontal bone is intersected below the frontal sinus. Anteriorly, the ethmoid air cells appear filled with respiratory mucosa. The ethmoid sinus air cells present stereotypical anterior, middle, and posterior divisions. The two superiormost extraocular muscles are present in this section along with the roof of the left oculus. Within the temporal fossa, the anterior temporalis presents vertically oriented fibers and the posterior temporalis fibers are horizontally arrayed. The frontal horns of the cerebral ventricles are intersected just above their transition to occipital and temporal horns.

Diagnostic Image. Coronal CT scan, showing anterior orbital and maxillary structures. The infundibulum (maxillary sinus) and sphenoethmoidal recess (sphenoid and ethmoid sinus), two mucus drainage paths, are well visualized.

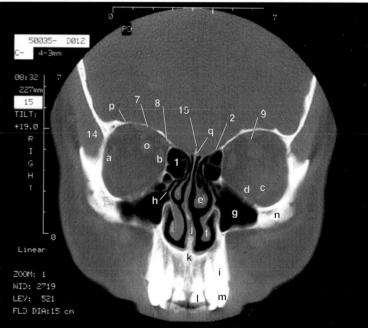

PLATE 8-2 SUPERIOR ORBIT *(Visible Man 1099)*

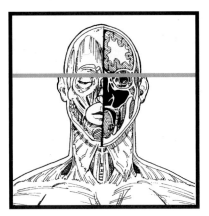

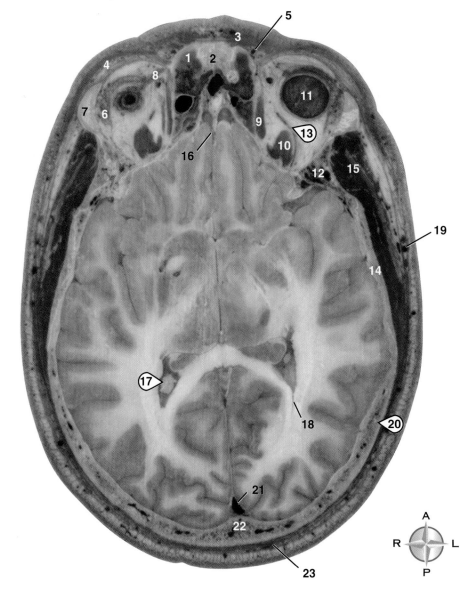

1 Mucosa of the anterior ethmoidal air cell
2 Cribriform plate of the ethmoid bone
3 Frontalis muscle
4 Orbicularis oculi muscle
5 Angular artery
6 Lacrimal gland
7 Zygomatic process of the frontal bone
8 Trochlea of the superior oblique muscle
9 Superior oblique muscle
10 Superior rectus muscle
11 Oculus (eye)
12 Greater wing of the sphenoid bone
13 Ophthalmic artery
14 Squamous portion of the temporal bone
15 Temporalis muscle
16 Crista galli of the ethmoid bone
17 Choroid plexus
18 Posterior horn of the lateral ventricle
19 Superficial temporal vessels
20 Diploe of the parietal bone

21 Superior sagittal sinus
22 Groove for the superior sagittal sinus on the occipital bone
23 Occipital muscle

RADIOGRAPH KEY

a Straight sinus
b Great cerebral vein (great vein of Galen)
c Inferior petrosal sinus

d Sigmoid sinus
e Transverse sinus
f Confluence of the sinuses
g Internal jugular vein
h Lamina papyracea

152

PLATE 8-2 SUPERIOR ORBIT (Visible Man 1099)

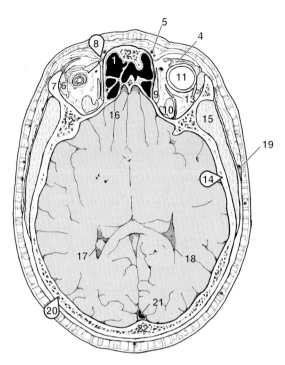

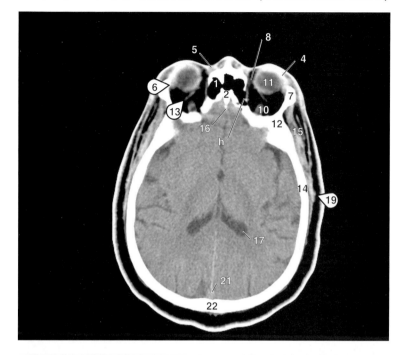

Corresponding CT. Areas of thin bone on the lateral walls of the ethmoid sinuses (i.e., the lamina papyracea), which externally form the medial walls of the orbits, appear as false holes, or "pseudoforamina." The partial-voluming (see Introduction) effect has caused these thin bone regions to "drop out" of the image.

Cryosection. Inferior to the superolateral orbit (frontal bone), on the left, is the lacrimal gland. Note that on the other side, the superior oblique muscle can be seen passing through the trochlea. The roofs of both occuli are now visible. The cerebral ventricles are just beginning to extend into the occipital horn, thus the transition to the temporal horns is not far inferior to this section.

Diagnostic Image. Midsagittal magnetic resonance (MR) angiogram illustrating cerebral venous sinus drainage. The entire 3D image volume is seen here as if it were a projection radiograph. In the midline (midsagittal plane), several bridging veins are seen draining into the superior sagittal sinus. The Great Cerebral Vein is seen draining into the straight sinus. The straight sinus meets the superior sagittal sinus at the confluence. Blood is flowing laterally out of the image plane in either direction through the transverse sinuses and then inferiorly toward the jugular foramen. The inferior petrosal sinus is also seen to drain to the weakly visualized internal jugular vein.

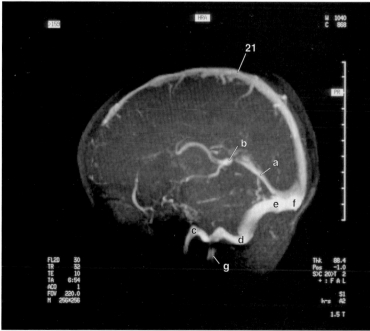

PLATE 8-3 MID-ORBIT *(Visible Man 1107)*

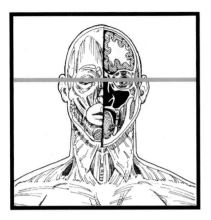

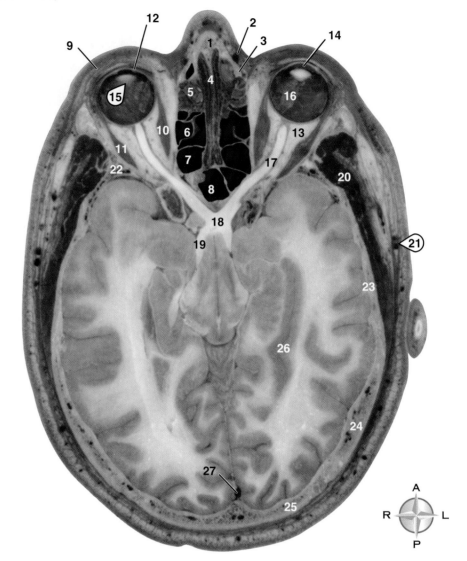

1   Nasal bones
2   Angular artery
3   Frontal process of the maxilla
4   Nasal septum
5   Anterior ethmoidal air cell
6   Middle ethmoidal air cell
7   Posterior ethmoidal air cell
8   Sphenoid sinus
9   Orbicularis oculi muscle
10 Medial rectus muscle
11 Lateral rectus muscle
12 Cornea
13 Extraocular fat
14 Anterior chamber
15 Lens
16 Vitreous body
17 Optic nerve
18 Optic chiasm

19 Optic tract
20 Temporalis muscle
21 Superficial temporal vessels
22 Greater wing of the sphenoid
23 Squamous portion of the
    temporal bone

24 Parietal bone
25 Occipital bone
26 Distal temporal horn of the
    lateral ventricles
27 Superior sagittal sinus

RADIOGRAPH KEY

a   Calcification of the pineal gland
b   Calcification of the choroid
    plexus

PLATE 8-3 MID-ORBIT *(Visible Man 1107)*

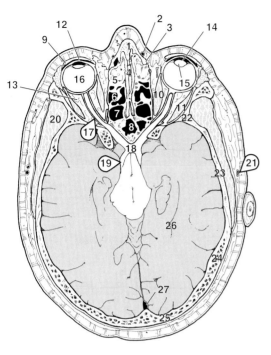

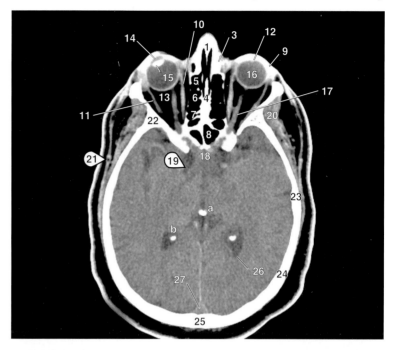

Corresponding CT. More of the thin bone on the ethmoid forming medial walls of the orbits have "dropped out" of the image. As in the cryosection, a single sphenoid air cell is seen just anterior to the optic chiasm. However, the sphenoid air cells are paired in the MR image. Note ossification of the choroid plexus and pineal gland, commonly seen in head films of adults.

Cryosection. Portion of the nasal septum underneath the "1" label is contributed by the ethmoid perpendicular plate. The separation between aqueous humor (anterior chamber) and vitreous humor (vitreous body) is visible on the left side. The orbital bone contributed by the sphenoid is thickened at the optic foramen lateral to both optic nerves. The optic chiasm covers the pituitary fossa (a.k.a. sella turcica). The ophthalmic arteries branch off the carotid arteries at the internal foramen to the optic canal, just inferior to the optic nerves. Nearly the entire temporal horn of the cerebral ventricle is intersected on the left. The third cerebral ventricle is present in the midline as a slit just posterior to the optic chiasm. The subcutaneous occipitalis muscles are visible posteriorly.

Corresponding MR. Axial MR scan highlighting (bright) fat within the orbits, especially around the optic nerve, medial rectus muscle, and lateral rectus muscle. The sphenoid sinus appears enlarged as the lucent air blends into the dark bone of the sphenoid body. Note the diploic spaces within the dark cortical bone, especially lateral to the optic canal and posteriorly. This plane shows the optic nerves approaching, but not reaching, the optic chiasm.

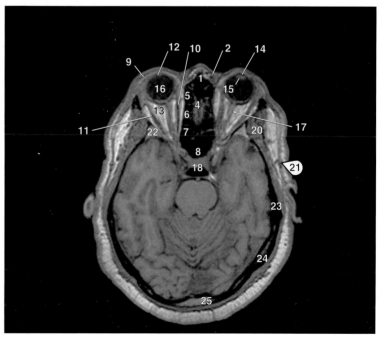

PLATE 8-4 INFERIOR ORBIT *(Visible Man 1118)*

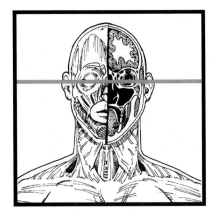

1   Nasal septum
2   Frontal process of the maxilla
3   Angular artery
4   Orbicularis oculi muscle
5   Tarsal plate
6   Nasolacrimal duct
7   Perpendicular plate of the ethmoid bone
8   Middle ethmoidal air cell
9   Posterior ethmoidal air cell
10 Sphenoid sinus
11 Inferior oblique muscle
12 Sclera
13 Inferior rectus muscle
14 Frontal process of the zygomatic bone
15 Greater wing of the sphenoid bone
16 Temporalis muscle
17 Superficial temporal vessels
18 Squamous portion of the temporal bone
19 Petrous portion of the temporal bone
20 Parietal bone
21 Occipital bone
22 Superior sagittal sinus
23 Auricular cartilage
24 Internal carotid artery
25 Cavernous sinus

RADIOGRAPH KEY

a   Levator palpebrae superioris muscle
b   Superior rectus muscle

c   Superior oblique muscle
d   Lateral rectus muscle
e   Medial rectus muscle
f   Olfactory tract
g   Optic nerve
h   Cerebrospinal fluid-filled space
i   Masseter muscle
j   Ethmoid sinus

k   Orbital fat
l   Perpendicular plate of the ethmoid bone
m   Sphenoethmoidal recess
n   Middle meatus
o   Inferior meatus
p   Hard palate with dentition
q   Nasal cavity

r   Infundibulum
s   Medial pterygoid muscle
t   Mandible with dentition
u   Genioglossus muscle
v   Mylohyoid muscle
w   Anterior belly of the digastric muscle
x   Inferior orbital fissure

PLATE 8-4 INFERIOR ORBIT (Visible Man 1118)

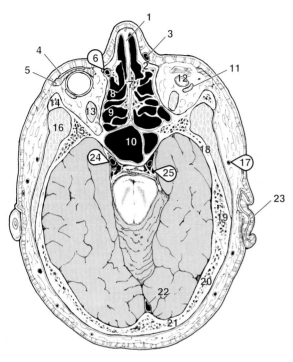

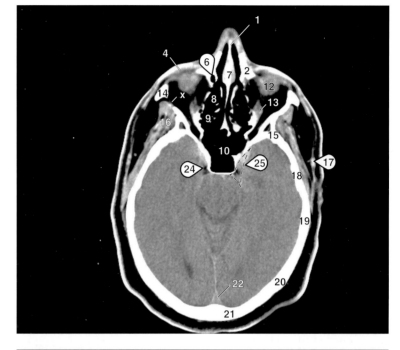

Corresponding CT. Despite their gracility, the three parts of the nasal septum are more distinct than in the cryosection image. The lateral extent of the inferior orbital tissue gives rise to an apparent "opening" in the lateralmost portion of the right orbit.

Cryosection. This plane intersects all components of the nasal septum: septal cartilage (1), ethmoid perpendicular plate (7), and vomer (8). Most likely, the maximum extent of the sphenoid sinus is seen within the sphenoid body. The carotid arteries are seen within the cavernous sinus. Posterior auricular and occipital vessels appear subcutaneously behind the ear.

Diagnostic Image. Coronal MR highlighting (bright) fatty elements taken just above the olfactory epithelium of the nasal cavity. The optic nerve and structures are highlighted by orbital fat. The ethmoid and maxillary paranasal sinus cavities are seen above and lateral to the nasal cavity, respectively. (The maxillary sinus drainage into the infundibulum below the middle meatus is bilaterally visible.) The dentition and alveoli have a negative signal. Note the optic nerve, which is gray with surrounding space that contains CSF. CSF also extends externally along the optic nerve.

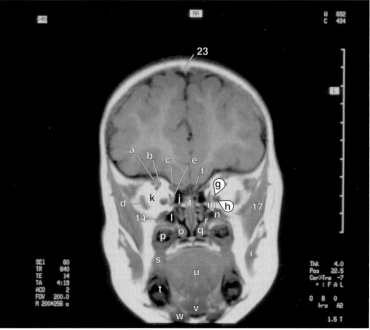

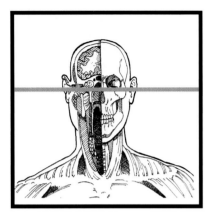

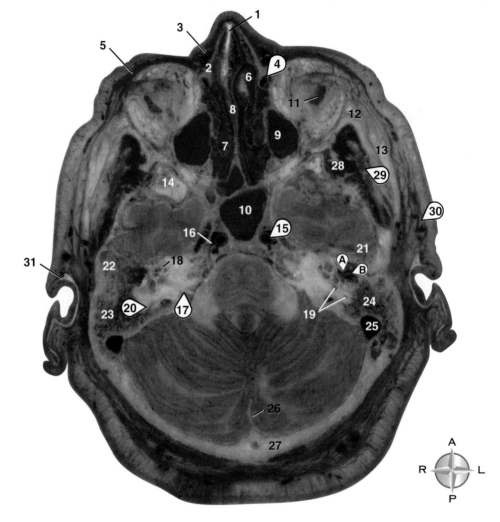

1 Cartilaginous nasal septum
2 Frontal process of the maxilla
3 Angular artery
4 Nasolacrimal duct
5 Orbicularis oculi muscle
6 Middle turbinate
7 Superior turbinate
8 Perpendicular plate of the ethmoid bone
9 Maxillary sinus
10 Sphenoid sinus
11 Inferior oblique muscle
12 Frontal process of the zygomatic bone
13 Zygomatic process of the temporal bone
14 Sphenoid bone
15 Internal carotid artery
16 Cavernous sinus
17 Cranial nerve VII and VIII
18 Cochlea of the inner ear
19 Anterior (superior) semicircular canal
20 Endolymphatic duct
21 Ear ossicles: A. stapes; B. malleolar-incal joint

22 Petrous portion of the temporal bone
23 Mastoid process of the temporal bone
24 Mastoid air cell
25 Sigmoid sinus
26 Falx cerebelli
27 Occipital bone

28 Temporalis muscle
29 Tendon of the temporalis muscle
30 Superficial temporal vessels
31 Tragus cartilage of the auricle

RADIOGRAPH KEY

a Posterior ethmoidal air cell
b Body of the sphenoid bone

c Middle cranial fossa
d Internal acoustic meatus
e Malleolar-incal joint
f Posterior cranial fossa
g Scalp
h Tympanic membrane
i External auditory meatus

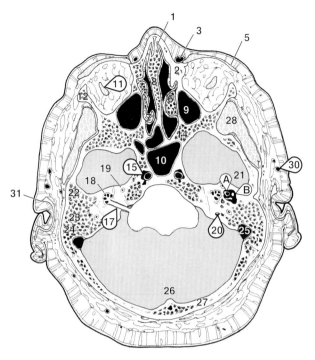

Corresponding CT. The section through the left ear is somewhat inferior to that of the right ear. Note the presence of the maxillary sinus, the zygomatic arch, and the middle-ear constituents on the right, whereas the nasolacrimal duct has not reached its inferior extent on left.

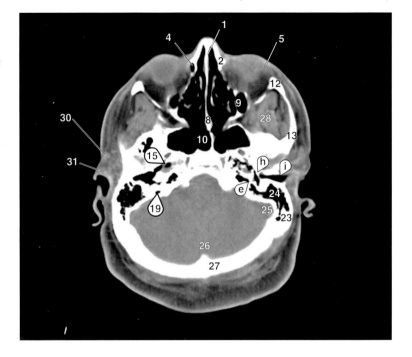

Cryosection. Posteriorly, the nasal septum forms from the intersection of the ethmoid perpendicular plate and vomer, whereas anteriorly, it is formed by the nasal septal cartilage. The floor of the orbit is anterior to the roof of the maxillary sinus. The carotid arteries can be seen emerging from the carotid canal in the middle cranial fossa.

Diagnostic Image. Axial CT through the upper petrous presents the uppermost right middle ear. The malleolar-incal joint is seen in the epitympanic recess. The roof of the internal acoustic meatus is bilaterally visible. Thin section CT scan offers exquisite detail of the bony structures of the middle and inner ear. (Key: A, anterior; L, left; P, posterior; R, right.)

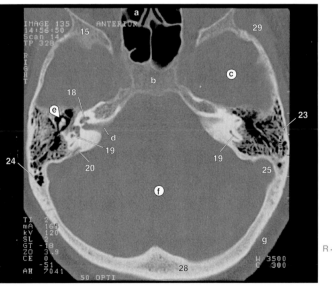

159

PLATE 8-6 PALATE, C1, AND C2 *(Visible Man 1168)*

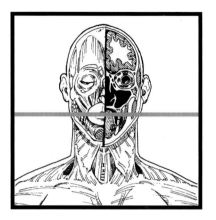

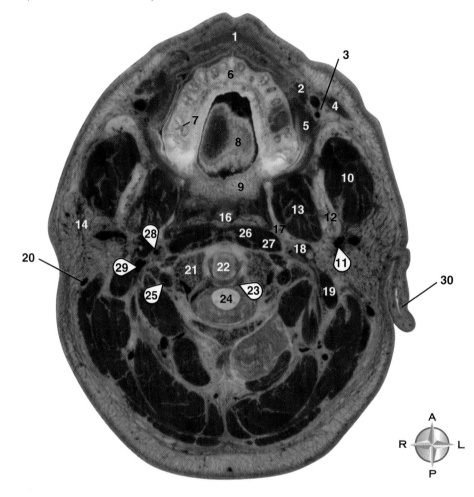

1 Orbicularis oris muscle
2 Levator anguli oris muscle
3 Facial artery and vein
4 Zygomaticus major muscle
5 Buccinator muscle
6 Maxilla
7 Alveolar process of the maxilla
8 Dorsum of the tongue
9 Soft palate (uvula apparent in radiographs)
10 Masseter muscle

11 Retromandibular vein
12 Ramus of the mandible
13 Lateral pterygoid muscle
14 Parotid gland
15 Superficial temporal vessels
16 Region of pharyngeal tubercle
17 Sphenoid bone
18 Stylohyoid ligament and muscle
19 Posterior belly of the digastric muscle
20 Occipital artery

21 First cervical vertebrae (Atlas)
22 Dens epistrophe of the second cervical vertebra (Axis)
23 Horizontal band of the cruciform ligament
24 Spinal cord
25 Vertebral artery in foramina transversaria
26 Longus colli muscle
27 Longus capitis muscle

28 Internal carotid artery
29 Internal jugular vein
30 Inferior portion of the helix of the auricle

RADIOGRAPH KEY

a Roof of the bony palate
b Palatoglossus muscle
c Palatopharyngeus muscle
d Bony palate

PLATE 8-6 Palate, C1, and C2 *(Visible Man 1168)*

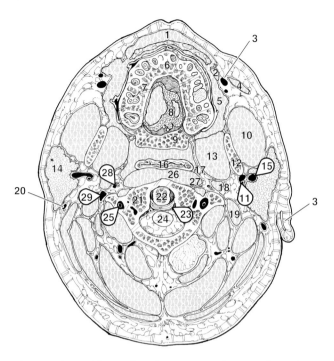

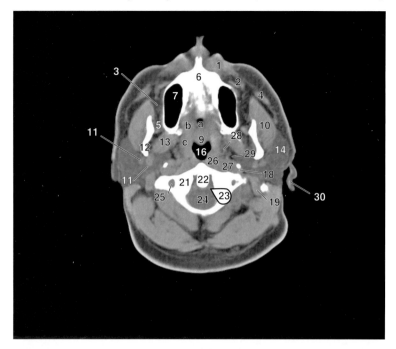

Corresponding CT. Incline of this plane through the first cervical vertebra and that of the diagnostic image (below) are higher anteriorly than that of the cryosection. Note that anteriorly the maxillary sinus, the roots of the anterior teeth, and the root of the nose are visible. Note that in this view, but not in the cryosection, the negative shadow (patency) and shape of the pharynx are seen as in a live patient.

Cryosection. The midline depression in the upper lip is the philtrum. Tooth root apices are seen in the alveoli inferior to the maxillary sinus. Some of the maxillary sinus mucosa is present on the left. The dens epistrophe of the axis (C2) sits anterior to the transverse band of the cruciform ligament and posterior to the anterior arch of the atlas (C1). Note that the vagus nerve is approximately sandwiched by the internal carotid artery and the jugular vein within the carotid sheath at this level. The lateral mass underlying the superior articular facet of the atlas is seen. Like that facet, it is narrow mediolaterally and elongates anteroposteriorly. The vertebral arteries can be seen to lie inside of the right and the left foramina transversaria of C1.

Corresponding MR. Axial MR image better matches the cryosection anteriorly than that of the corresponding CT, as both cut through the upper lip. The lip is significantly thicker (anteroposteriorly) in the MR image. There is some distortion in the anterior dental arcade, probably from metallic dental artifact in the region of the palate. The lumens of the carotid, vertebral, and maxillary arteries are bright. There is a greater traverse of the posterior digastric muscle on the left than on the right. The uvula is more apparent than in the cryosection. The dens and ligaments around it are easily visualized.

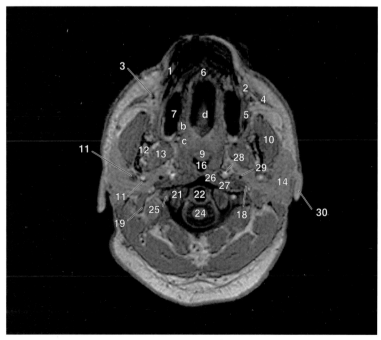

161

PLATE 8-7 LOWER MANDIBLE, C2, AND C3 *(Visible Man 1215)*

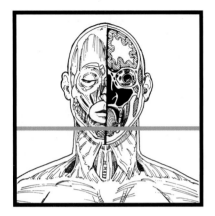

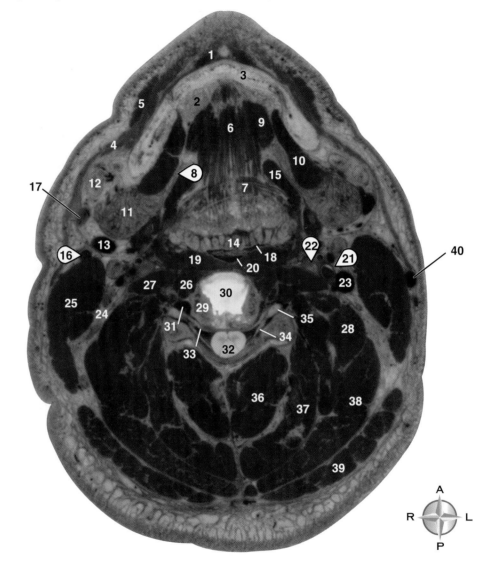

1   Mentalis muscle
2   Sublingual gland
3   Mandible
4   Platysma muscle
5   Depressor anguli inferioris muscle
6   Genioglossus muscle
7   Hyoglossus muscle
8   Submandibular duct
9   Mylohyoid muscle
10 Anterior belly of the digastric muscle
11 Submandibular gland
12 Parotid gland
13 Retromandibular vein
14 Lingual tonsil
15 Medial pterygoid muscle
16 Maxillary artery
17 Superficial temporal vessels
18 Paraglottic space of the pharynx
19 Superior pharyngeal constrictor muscle
20 Alar fascia
21 Internal carotid artery
22 Vagus nerve
23 Internal jugular vein
24 Path of the occipital artery
25 Sternocleidomastoid muscle
26 Longus capitis muscle

27 Longus colli muscle
28 Longissimus capitis muscle
29 Third cervical vertebrae
30 Intervertebral disk (between second and third cervical vertebrae)
31 Vertebral artery

32 Spinal cord
33 Ventral ramus
34 Dorsal ramus
35 Dorsal root ganglion
36 Erector spinae muscle
37 Semispinalis cervicis muscle
38 Semispinalis capitis muscle

39 Trapezius muscle
40 External jugular vein

RADIOGRAPH KEY

a   Palatopharyngeus muscle

PLATE 8-7 LOWER MANDIBLE, C2, AND C3 *(Visible Man 1215)*

Corresponding CT. The palatopharyngeal arch is highlighted by air in the oropharynx. The pharynx in this live subject is significantly more patent than it is in the cryosection. Genioglossal spines can be seen on the deep surface of the mandibular symphysis.

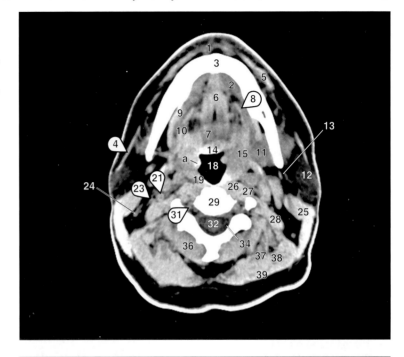

Cryosection. Bilateral genioglossus muscles can be seen coming from their right and left genial pit origins on the internal border of the mandible. A portion of the submandibular gland is seen wrapping around the posterior free edge and onto the superior surface of the left mylohyoid muscle. The right submandibular duct is making its way to a single papilla alongside the lingual frenulum. The alar fascia can be seen to stretch behind the superior constrictor and in front of the prevertebral muscles. There are some openings in the "danger space," which are usually only potential spaces in the living patient.

Diagnostic Image. Axial CT highlighting (dashed circle) a benign submandibular growth (dermoid cyst) on right. Note the posterior displacement of the right side pharynx, C4, and its associated structures. Contrast of blood vessels highlights carotid sheath and vertebral arteries within foramina transversaria. Posterior rotation of the right side of the neck is typically just positional, but can be a response to neck pain.

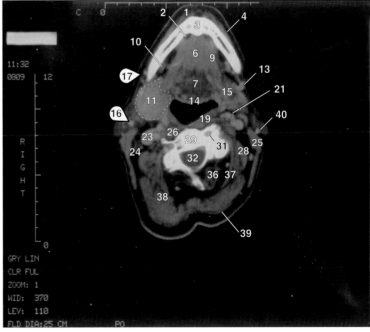

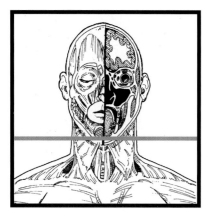

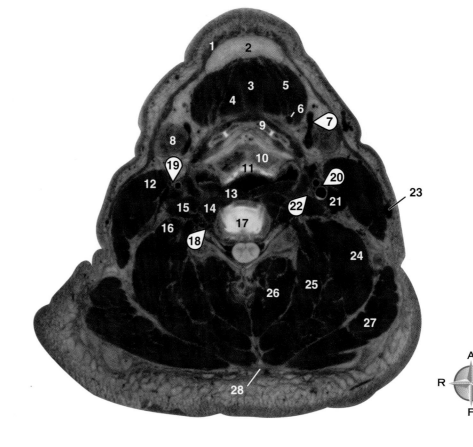

1   Platysma muscle
2   Mandible
3   Geniohyoid muscle
4   Mylohyoid muscle
5   Anterior belly of the digastric muscle
6   Posterior belly of the digastric muscle
7   Lingual artery
8   Submandibular gland
9   Hyoid bone
10 Vallecula
11 Epiglottis
12 Sternocleidomastoid muscle
13 Superior pharyngeal constrictor muscle
14 Longus capitis muscle
15 Longus colli muscle
16 Anterior scalene muscle
17 Fourth cervical vertebrae
18 Vertebral artery
19 Phrenic nerve
20 Bifurcation of the common carotid artery
21 Internal jugular vein
22 Vagus nerve (c. X)
23 External jugular vein
24 Semispinalis capitis muscle

25 Semispinalis cervicis muscle
26 Erector spinae muscle
27 Trapezius muscle
28 Ligamentum nuchae

RADIOGRAPH KEY

a   Adenoid tonsil
b   Sphenoid bone
c   Cruciform ligament
d   Inferior nasal concha
e   Choanae
f   Tensor veli palatini muscle

g   Uvula
h   Nasal mucosa
i   Hard palate
j   Foramen cecum
k   Superior pharyngeal constrictor muscle
l   Middle pharyngeal constrictor muscle
m   Inferior pharyngeal constrictor muscle
n   Spinal cord

o   Vallecula
p   Intrinsic muscles of the tongue
q   Epiglottis
r   Genioglossus muscle
s   Hyoglossus muscle
t   Thyroid gland
u   Esophagus
v   Laryngeal cartilage
w   Cricoid cartilage
x   Trachea
y   Thyroglossal duct cyst

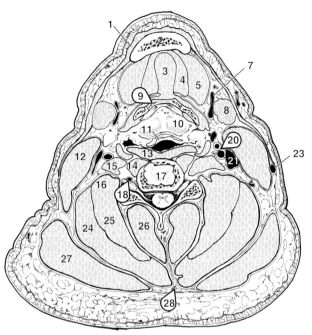

Corresponding CT. Digastric spines can again be seen on the deep surface of the mandibular symphysis. The foramina transversaria housing the vertebral arteries are well visualized.

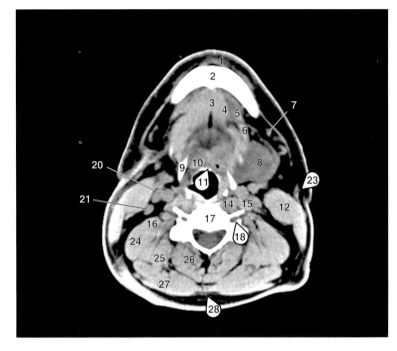

Cryosection. Anterior belly of the digastric muscle inserts just below the mylohyoid muscle at the mental symphysis. Often, a spine of bone is inside this insertion. The platysma muscle, which inserts into the skin of the neck, arises superficial to the base of the base of the mandible. One of the most inferior branches of the external carotid, the lingual artery can be seen approaching the tongue from below. The common carotid bifurcation occurs just inferior to this level, approximately at the superior edge of the thyroid cartilage. This section passes through the junction between the lesser horn of the hyoid and the hyoid body. The space anterior to the epiglottis is referred to as the vallecula. The space between the epiglottis and the middle constrictor medially is the laryngeal inlet. The two spaces laterally enter the right and the left piriform recesses.

Diagnostic Image. Midsagittal MR highlighting (dashed shape) a thyroglossal duct cyst. It has an intermediate position between the foramen cecum origin of the thyroid gland and its final position anterior to the larynx. The vallecular, supraglottic, and infraglottic spaces are well visualized.

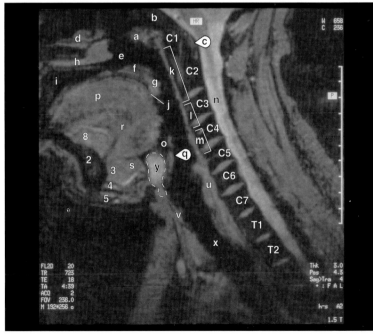

CHAPTER 9

The Neck

INTRODUCTION

Geometrically, the neck can be thought of as a columnar structure housing several tubular structures. From anterior to posterior there is a cylindrical superficial nuchal muscle plane formed by the strap muscles, the sternocleidomastoid, the scalenes, the splenius, the semispinalis capitis, and the trapezius. Each of these muscles has superficial and deep investing layers of fascia. Three deep fascial columns lie within the superficial muscular-fascial column. Anteriorly, the pretracheal fascia surrounds the visceral column housing the larynx, trachea, constrictor muscles, esophagus, recurrent vagus nerves, thyroid and parathyroid glands, and thyroid vasculature. Lateral to the visceral column are two carotid sheaths enclosing the (medial to lateral) common carotid artery, vagus nerve, and internal jugular vein.

The superior extent of the neck anteriorly is the inferior border of the mandibular corpus and the ramus continuing posteriorly onto the supramastoid crest and nuchal lines. The neck's inferior limit is the thoracic inlet. Many primarily cervical structures cross these boundaries. Levels in the neck are usually referred to the vertebral skeleton, but on occasion, the laryngeal skeleton is useful. Although all the cervical vertebrae present foramina transversaria housing vertebral arteries, the position of these foramina and much of the rest of their morphology changes drastically. The first two cervical vertebrae, the atlas and axis, present several specializations for head movement. The fourth through the sixth cervical vertebrae have an especially large neural canal housing the cervical enlargement, a concomitant of the brachial plexus.

The seventh cervical vertebra, vertebra prominens, has a long stout vertebral process and more horizontally oriented transverse processes, a morphology that is transitional to thoracic vertebral morphology. Since the rib cage slopes anteroinferiorly the anterior portion of the thoracic inlet is found below the seventh cervical vertebra.

An anterior view of the contents of the visceral column and both carotid sheaths is seen in Figure 9-1. As shown in Figure 9-1, the blood supply of neck structures derives primarily from branches of the subclavian (1) and external carotid arteries (24). The laryngeal skeleton and the tracheal rings

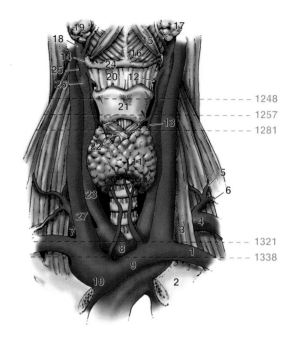

may be used to determine craniocaudal level in the neck. For example, the bifurcation of the common carotid (23) is most often associated with the superior edge of the thyroid cartilage (21). The coronal magnetic resonance (MR) scan in Plate 4 highlights these blood vessels.

The first plate of this chapter is an image of the area inferior to the hyoid bone and inferior mandible edge and that passes through the supraglottic (above the vocal folds) portion of the thyroid cartilage. Plate 2 images the area that passes directly through the vocal folds (glottis) and then through the thyroid cartilage. Plates 4 and 5 pass through the root of the neck at thoracic vertebral levels T1 and T2.

Swellings of the neck are somewhat common and are most often located in the lymph nodes concentrated along the internal jugular vein. The diagnostic images associated with Plates 1 and 3 show masses that have to do with non-lymphatic swellings. The coronal MR-scan of the larynx with section 2 presents an informative view of this structure.

PLATE 9-1 Thyroid Cartilage and Supraglottic Structures *(Visible Man 1248)*

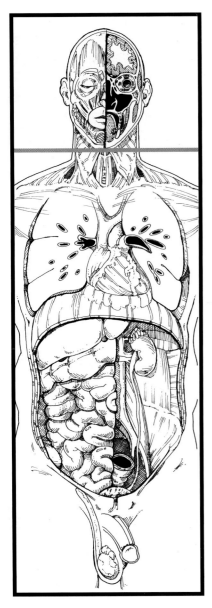

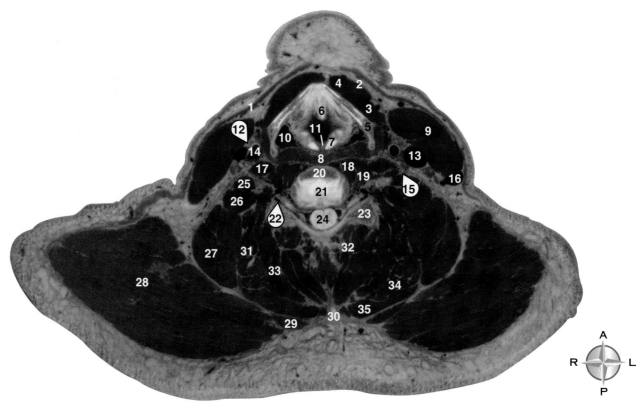

1 Platysma muscle
2 Omohyoid muscle
3 Sternothyroid muscle
4 Sternohyoid muscle
5 Thyroid cartilage
6 Epiglottis
7 Arytenoid cartilage
8 Inferior constrictor muscle
9 Sternocleidomastoid muscle
10 Piriform recess
11 Aryepiglottic fold
12 Vagus nerve
13 Internal jugular vein
14 Common carotid artery
15 Phrenic nerve

16 External jugular vein
17 Anterior scalene muscle
18 Longus capitis muscle
19 Longus colli muscle
20 Fifth cervical vertebra
21 Intervertebral disc between the fourth and the fifth cervical vertebrae
22 Vertebral artery
23 Transverse process of the fifth cervical vertebra
24 Spinal cord
25 Middle scalene muscle
26 Posterior scalene muscle
27 Levator scapulae muscle

28 Trapezius muscle
29 Rhomboid minor muscle
30 Nuchal ligament
31 Longissimus capitis muscle
32 Transversospinalis muscle of the erector spinae muscle group
33 Semispinalis cervicis muscle
34 Semispinalis capitis muscle
35 Splenius muscle

RADIOGRAPH KEY

a 100-cc lateral neck mass
b Spinous process of the fifth cervical vertebra

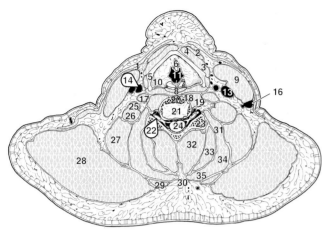

Cryosection. This section passes through the center of the intervertebral disc between the fourth and the fifth cervical vertebra. The semicircular, midline tissue mass anterior to the platysma is commonly found submental adipose (fat) tissue. The common carotid artery seen here commonly divides into its internal and external carotid branches immediately superior to this level, at the top of the thyroid cartilage. Note that the vagus nerve has passed anteriorly in the carotid sheath, between the common carotid artery and the internal jugular vein. It lies posterior to these vessels at levels superior to this after its emergence from the skull at the jugular foramen. Virtually no right external jugular vein exists, whereas the large external jugular vein on the left wraps internally around the posterior sternocleidomastoid muscle border. Variability in external jugular vein morphology, between individuals or between the right and the left sides of one individual, is common. Note that the suboccipital muscles are in a section superior to that seen here (e.g., Chapter 6, Plate 6-1).

Corresponding CT. The esophagus, constricted by the laryngeal apparatus, is not patent at this level. Note that the posterior axillary fold creases the thick and fibrous fatty layer of tissue on the dorsum of the neck and upper back.

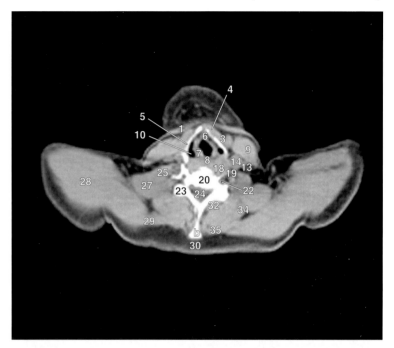

Diagnostic Image. CT scan highlighting a large cyst below the platysma. Branchial cysts (of embryological branchial arch origin) are usually more strongly encapsulated than this.

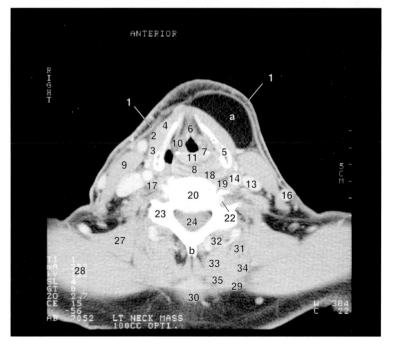

PLATE 9-2 RIMA GLOTTIDUS *(Visible Man 1257)*

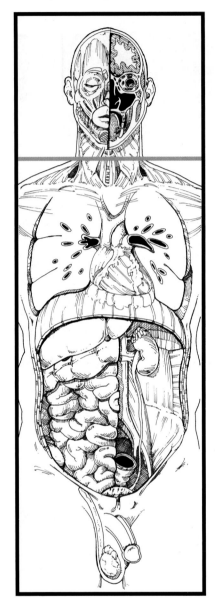

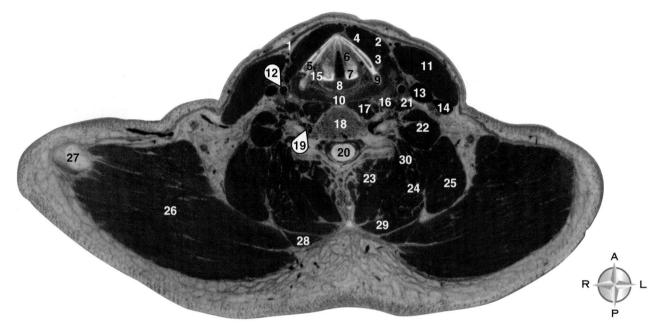

1	Platysma muscle
2	Omohyoid muscle
3	Sternothyroid muscle
4	Sternohyoid muscle
5	Thyroid cartilage
6	Rima glottidis
7	Arytenoid cartilage
8	Posterior cricoarytenoid muscle
9	Inferior horn of the thyroid cartilage
10	Inferior constrictor muscle
11	Sternocleidomastoid muscle
12	Common carotid artery
13	Internal jugular vein
14	External jugular vein
15	Cricothyroid muscle
16	Longus colli muscle
17	Longus capitis muscle
18	Fifth cervical vertebra
19	Vertebral artery

20	Spinal cord
21	Anterior scalene muscle
22	Middle and posterior scalene muscles
23	Erector spinae muscle
24	Semispinalis cervicis muscle
25	Levator scapulae muscle
26	Trapezius muscle
27	Acromion process of the scapula
28	Rhomboid minor muscle
29	Splenius muscle
30	Longissimus capitis muscle

RADIOGRAPH KEY

a	Nasopharynx
b	Dens epistrophe of the second cervical vertebra
c	Medulla
d	Cerebellum
e	Oropharynx

f	Ligamentum nuchae
g	Laryngopharynx
h	Soft palate
i	Genioglossus muscle
j	Geniohyoid muscle
k	Mylohyoid muscle
l	Epiglottis
m	Lamina of the thyroid cartilage
n	Level of the true vocal cords
o	Arch of the cricoid cartilage
p	Trachea
q	Lamina of the cricoid cartilage
r	Esophagus
s	Spinous process of the seventh cervical vertebra "vertebra prominans"
C	Cervical vertebrae followed by the corresponding number
T	Thoracic vertebrae followed by the corresponding number

PLATE 9-2 RIMA GLOTTIDUS (Visible Man 1257)

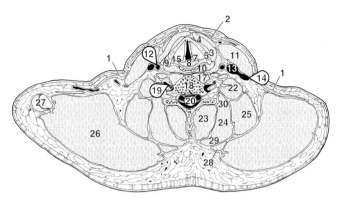

Corresponding CT. The cranial edges of both scapular vertebral borders (supraspinatus fossa) are seen here, but not in the cryosection. This may be mistaken for the first rib, which will be found more anteriorly in proximity to the thoracic inlet. Note the carotid artery on the left. The adjacent left jugular vein is collapsed.

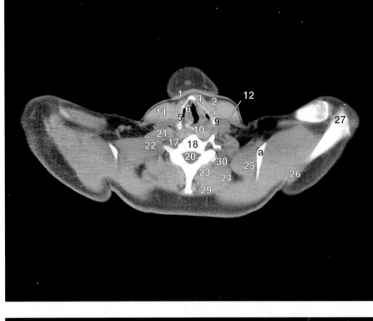

Cryosection. This section passes through the fifth cervical vertebra. The level of the true vocal fold intersects the largest extent of the arytenoid cartilages. Both the lateral extension of the muscular process and the anterior extension of the vocal process are seen at this level (note L shape). The vestibular (false vocal) folds intercept the more limited vertical process of the arytenoid cartilages. The brachial plexus emerges between the anterior and the middle scalene muscles and is traveling laterally in the connective tissue seen between the sternocleidomastoid and the trapezius muscles.

Corresponding MR. Submental fatty tissue, not seen in the cryosection, is highlighted here, but not in the corresponding CT image. Note that the laryngeal cartilage and the dense compact bone of the vertebra appear dark, but this does not indicate a space.

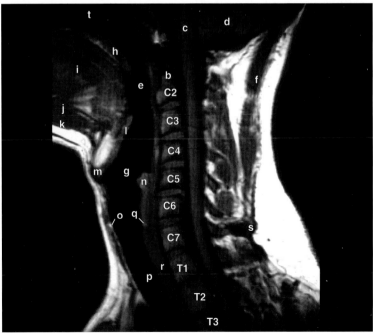

PLATE 9-3 BASE CRICOID CARTILAGE (*Visible Man 1281*)

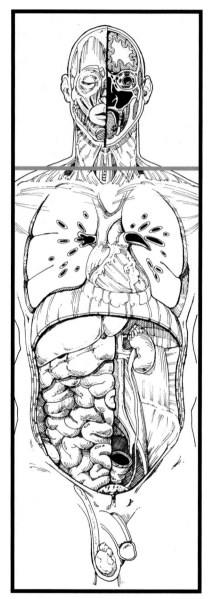

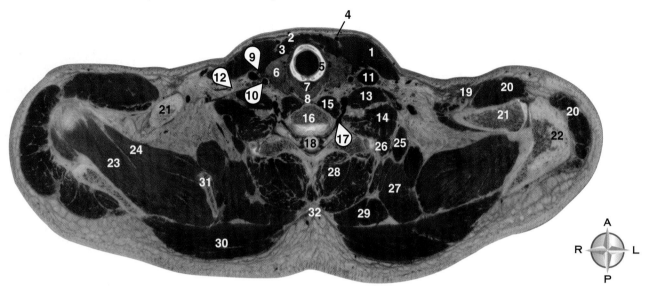

1	Sternocleidomastoid muscle
2	Sternohyoid muscle
3	Sternothyroid muscle
4	Anterior jugular vein
5	Cricoid cartilage
6	Thyroid gland
7	Esophagus
8	Cricopharyngeus muscle
9	Vagus nerve
10	Common carotid artery
11	Internal jugular vein
12	Phrenic nerve

13	Anterior scalene muscle
14	Middle and posterior scalene muscle
15	Longus colli muscle
16	Sixth cervical vertebra
17	Dorsal root ganglion
18	Spinal cord
19	Pectoralis major muscle
20	Deltoid muscle
21	Clavicle
22	Acromion process of the scapula
23	Supraspinatus muscle

24	Subscapularis muscle
25	Longissimus capitis muscle
26	Longissimus cervicis muscle
27	Levator scapulae muscle
28	Erector spinae muscle
29	Rhomboid minor muscle
30	Trapezius muscle
31	Scapular spine
32	Nuchal ligament

RADIOGRAPH KEY

a Thyroid cyst

PLATE 9-3 BASE CRICOID CARTILAGE (*Visible Man 1281*)

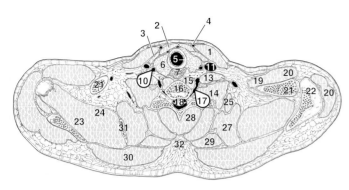

Corresponding CT. This section passes through the seventh cervical vertebrae. Note the long spinous process that results in its name: vertebra prominens. Although the vertebral level is slightly inferior to the cryosection, the laryngeal skeletal level is slightly superior to the complete ring of the cricoid seen in the cryosection. This is evidenced by the incomplete cricoid ring and the cricothyroid joint, visible on the left. Both supraspinatus fossae and muscles are clearly visualized. Note that unlike the cryosection, both humeral heads and scapular spines are present.

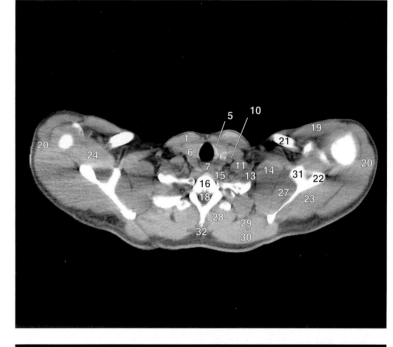

Cryosection. This section passes through base of the sixth cervical vertebra. Note the completely closed ring formed by the cricoid cartilage. The tracheal rings begin just inferior to this level. Behind it is a thickening of the lowest portion of inferior constrictor muscle, commonly referred to as the cricopharyngeus muscle. The longitudinally oriented muscular portion of the esophagus begins just inferior to the cricopharyngeus muscle. The left shoulder presents the acromioclavicular joint, whereas the right shoulder view is inferior to that joint. Therefore, supraspinatus can be seen passing onto the humeral head on the right. Note that all three portions of the deltoid muscle are simultaneously visible on the right, whereas the posterior portion is not visible on the left.

Diagnostic Image. CT image of a section that passes through base of the sixth cervical vertebra. The spinous process is not as long as that of the seventh cervical vertebra. There is a large thyroid mass on the right side. It has displaced the trachea and esophagus laterally to the left. It has also spread the carotid sheath so that the internal jugular vein and common carotid artery are no longer adjacent. Note the brightness of the vessels due to the presence of iodinated intravenous contrast. The thyroid gland is also bright due to its iodine content.

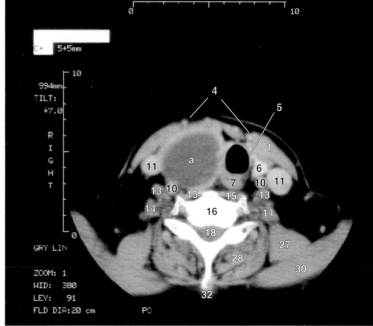

173

PLATE 9-4 THORACIC INLET AND JUGULAR NOTCH *(Visible Man 1321)*

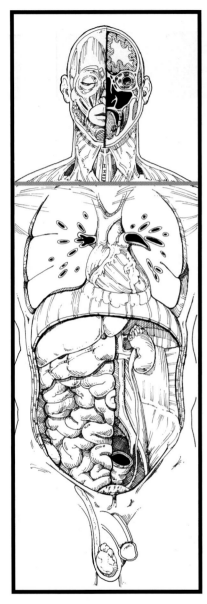

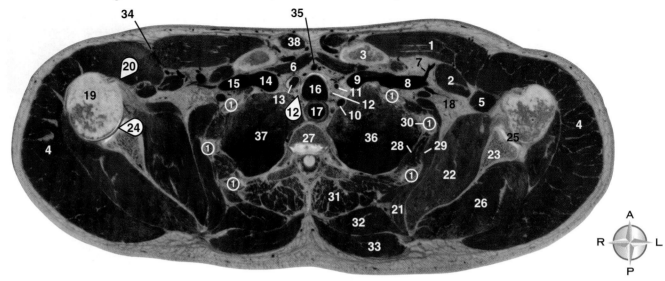

1	Pectoralis major muscle	21	Serratus anterior muscle
2	Pectoralis minor muscle	22	Subscapularis muscle
3	Clavicle	23	Scapula
4	Deltoid muscle	24	Glenoid fossa
5	Coracobrachialis muscle	25	Glenohumeral joint
6	Sternothyroid muscle	26	Infraspinatus muscle
7	Left thoracoacromial vein	27	First thoracic vertebra
8	Left subclavian vein	28	Internal intercostal muscle
9	Left brachiocephalic vein	29	External intercostal muscle
10	Left subclavian artery	30	Rib (corresponding rib numbers
11	Left common carotid artery		are within circles)
12	Recurrent laryngeal nerve	31	Erector spinae
13	Brachiocephalic artery	32	Rhomboid major muscle
14	Right brachiocephalic vein	33	Trapezius muscle
15	Right subclavian vein	34	Cephalic vein
16	Trachea	35	Right common carotid artery
17	Esophagus	36	Left lung
18	Brachial plexus	37	Right lung
19	Humerus	38	Sternocleidomastoid muscle
20	Long tendon of the biceps muscle		

RADIOGRAPH KEY

a Arch of the aorta
b Right common carotid artery
c Dorsal scapular artery
d Internal carotid artery (right and left)
e Superior vena cava
f Internal jugular vein
g Axillary vein
h External jugular vein
i Transverse cervical vein
j Anterior jugular vein
k Occipital vein
l Vertebral artery
m External carotid artery branches
n External carotid artery
o Coracoid process of the scapula
p Bicipital groove of the humerus

PLATE 9-4 THORACIC INLET AND JUGULAR NOTCH *(Visible Man 1321)*

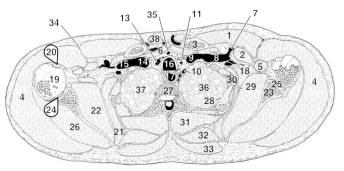

Corresponding CT. The trachea is shifted posteriorly to the right of the esophagus. Both right and left bicipital grooves, clavicular heads, coracoid processes, and glenoid fossae are well visualized. Also, note both the vertebral body and the transverse process facet for the left first rib.

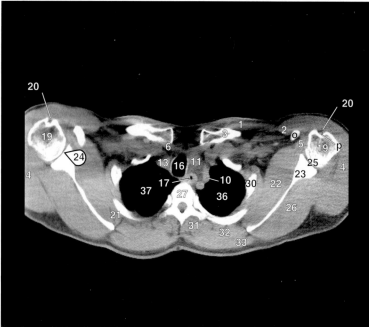

Cryosection. This section passes through the base of the first thoracic vertebra. This is also the level of the manubrioclavicular joint. Note that unlike the cricoid cartilage, the tracheal rings are not closed at rear. Right–left asymmetry is expected at this level between the brachiocephalic and the left common carotid or the subclavian arteries. The elongate left subclavian vein must cross the great arch to reach its counterpart on the right side to form the superior vena cava. The spinal cord is reduced in size versus the cervical enlargement, seen superiorly, for upper limb innervation. Note the extent to which the humeral head is situated within the glenoid fossa. It is held in place primarily by the rotator cuff (supraspinatus, infraspinatus, teres major, subscapularis) and deltoid muscles. Rib numbers are circled on the cryosection image.

Diagnostic Image. MR angiogram (MRA) highlights the great arch and its branches. The superior vena cava is seen to form from the two brachiocephalic veins. Note the great length of the left brachiocephalic vein as opposed to that of the right. Note the relationship of the arteries and veins. This angiogram was taken after injection of contrast agent had enhanced both the arterial and venous systems.

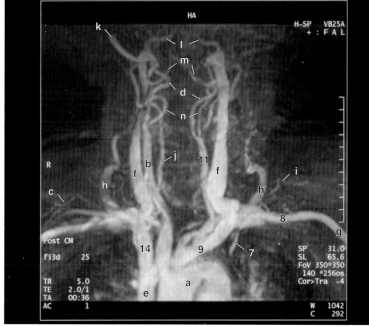

PLATE 9-5 LOWEST MANUBRIOCLAVICULAR JOINT *(Visible Man 1338)*

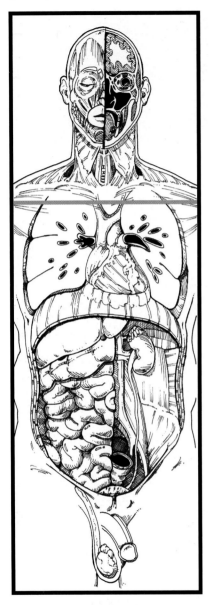

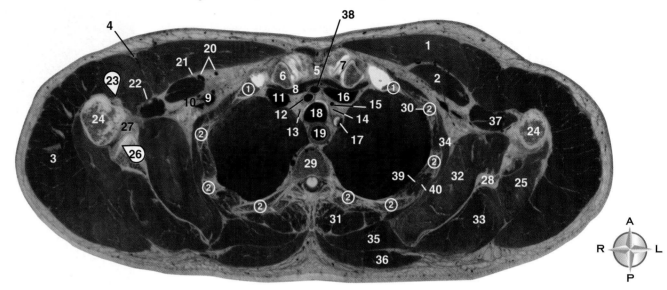

1	Pectoralis major muscle	
2	Pectoralis minor muscle	
3	Deltoid muscle	
4	Cephalic vein	
5	Manubrium (jugular notch)	
6	Clavicle	
7	Manubroclavicular joint	
8	Sternothyroid muscle	
9	Axillary vein	
10	Brachial plexus	
11	Right brachiocephalic vein	
12	Right subclavian artery	
13	Right recurrent laryngeal nerve	
14	Left recurrent laryngeal nerve	
15	Left common carotid artery	
16	Left subclavian vein	
17	Left subclavian artery	
18	Trachea	
19	Esophagus	
20	Thoracoacromial vessels	
21	Lateral pectoral nerve	

22	Medial pectoral nerve
23	Long head of the biceps muscle
24	Humerus
25	Teres major muscle
26	Glenoid fossa of the scapula
27	Glenohumeral joint
28	Scapula
29	Second thoracic vertebrae
30	Rib (corresponding rib numbers are within circles)
31	Erector spinae muscle
32	Subscapularis muscle
33	Infraspinatus muscle
34	Serratus anterior muscle
35	Rhomboid major muscle
36	Trapezius muscle
37	Coracobrachialis muscle
38	Right common carotid artery
39	Internal intercostal muscle
40	External intercostal muscle

RADIOGRAPH KEY

a	Tongue
b	Pharynx
c	Internal jugular vein
d	Sternocleidomastoid muscle
e	Common carotid artery
f	Superior vena cava
g	Arch of the aorta
h	Internal thoracic artery
i	Internal thoracic vein
j	Acromion process of the scapula
k	Coracoid process of the scapula
l	Insertion of the coracobrachialis muscle
m	Axillary artery
n	Lateral cord
o	Musculocutaneous nerve
p	Median nerve

PLATE 9-5 LOWEST MANUBRIOCLAVICULAR JOINT *(Visible Man 1338)*

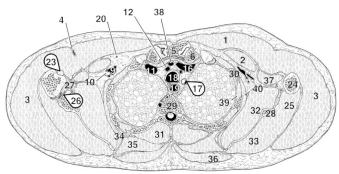

Cryosection. This section passes through the base of the top of the second thoracic vertebra. The lowest portion of the manubrioclavicular joint is seen. Also seen is the junction of the first rib and its cartilage as it approaches the manubrium. The second rib cartilage finds the manubriosternal angle inferior to this level. The proximity of the right subclavian and the common carotid arteries suggest that the brachiocephalic artery is just inferior to this level. An athlerosclerotic plaque, visible in the previous (superior) plate, now seems to fill the majority of the left subclavian lumen. These vessels have just emerged from the roof of the great arch of the aorta. The terminal ends of the long left and the shorter right brachiocephalic veins have nearly joined at this level. They drain into the superior vena cava immediately inferior. The inferiormost origin of the sternothyroid is visible as a thin slip anterior to these structures. Rib numbers are circled in the cryosection image.

Corresponding CT. CT scan of a rightward posterior shift of the trachea that has it now adjacent and to the left of the esophagus. The left side is a little lower at the shoulder, thus it is easier to see separation between the pectoralis minor and the coracobrachialis muscles as both make their way superiorly to the coracoid process. Note the vertebral body and the transverse process facet articulating with the head and tubercle of the left second rib. Also visible are the costal ends of the first ribs.

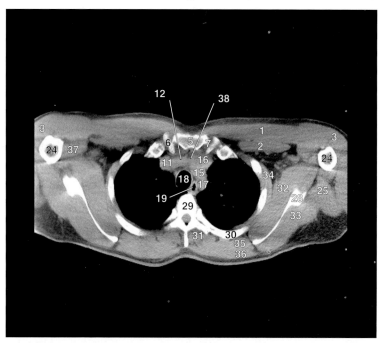

Diagnostic MR. MR highlighting bone, muscle, cartilage, and nerves. It is a coronal section through the neck and the superior mediastinum. The right subclavian artery is clearly visualized. Note three portions of the brachial plexus can be seen in approximation with this artery: the lateral cord, the musculocutaneous nerve, and the median nerve. (Used with permission from Lewin J: Imaging of the infrahyoid neck. Neuroimaging Clinics of North America; 1:219–234, 1998; Fig. 16.)

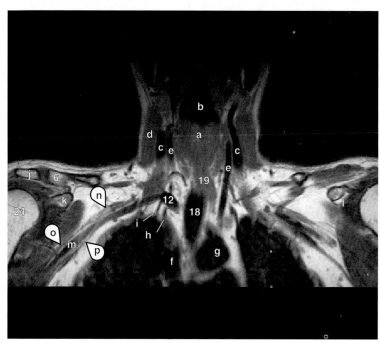

INDEX